jumbo
Bible
word search
collection
Volume 2

BARBOUR
PUBLISHING, INC.
Uhrichsville, Ohio

© MCMXCIX by Barbour Publishing, Inc.

ISBN 1-57748-611-0

Published by Barbour Publishing, Inc., P.O. Box 719, Uhrichsville, Ohio 44683 http://www.barbourbooks.com

 Member of the
Evangelical Christian
Publishers Association

Printed in the United States of America.

jumbo
Bible
word search
collection
Volume 2

1

Seen in Dreams & Visions

ANANIAS	ELIJAH	MOSES
ANGELS	EYES	PEACE
BASKET	FIRE	SCROLL
BEAST	GOLD	SHEET
BIRDS	GRAPES	SILVER
BONES	HEAVEN	SPIRIT
BOWL	HORN	STARS
BREAD	HORSE	SUN
CHERUBS	IDOLS	TEMPLE
CLAY	IRON	THRONE
COAL	LADDER	TREE
CORN	LAMB	VIAL
COWS	LOAF	WHEELS
CUP	LORD	
DRAGON	MOON	

```
S F R E K N S H E A V E N B O
L U A J R W O H Z M O O N U K
O E N O O I A O S B A S K E T
D C C C L J F R T E M P L E E
I A S A I N A N A T S T B O S
B E M L E N O R H T F O I T R
R P E G T A S E P A R G M I O
E M O S R S B U R E H C M R H
A L A S L E Q Z S D R I B I N
D E T E L L D L L S R C P P O
B R E E S E L D A A I A L S R
O H O E E C G O A M I L G A I
W B Y L W H O N R L B V V O Y
L E S R A T S A A C T R E E N
C U P S E N O B L H S G S L R
```

Bonus Trivia

Does the Bible say that all men have saving faith?

No! 2 Thessalonians 3:2 explicitly states, ".. .For all men have not faith."

5

2

Draw...

ANGER	MOUNT TABOR
BACK	NEAR
BATTLE	NET
BOW	NIGH
BREAST	OUT
CAMELS	RIVER
CITY	SOUL
DAGGER	SPEAR
DISCIPLES	SWORD
GATES	TONGUE
GOD	TRUE HEART
HITHER	VESSELS
INIQUITY	WATER
JORDAN	YEARS
LEVIATHAN	UNDERSTANDING

```
X C W A T E R E G N A T Z G G
S Y T I U Q I N I P K X N O S
W R O B A T T N U O M I D L R
E D R O W S D B O N D Y E E A
U A E B C I T Y R N I V G T E
G B B L T D I V A E I G R W Y
N A N U T J I T N A A A H O R
O C G F S T S S T D E S S B H
T K R G L R A H C H Y E T I N
S N E T E D A B E I T C T Z A
L X M D S N I U R A P H M I D
E S N Y S K R K G E E L W P R
M U O B E T W E R R V B E T O
A D M U V M L N E A R I U S J
C V C K L S P E A R Z O R T T
```

◇ **Bonus Trivia**

What languages were used in the sign over
the cross of Christ?

Hebrew, Greek, and Latin (John 19:20)

7

3

Enter...

CHAMBERS	GLORY	PEACE
CITY	HEAVEN	POSSESS
CLOSET	HOLIEST	REINS
CONGREGATION	HOST	REST
CONTENTION	HOUSE	ROCK
CURSE	JOY	ROOF
EARS	JUDGMENT	SANCTUARY
EGYPT	KINGDOM	STRAIT
FIELDS	LAND	SWORD
FORTRESS	LIFE	TEMPLE
GATES	LODGINGS	TENT
GILGAL	PATH	WINDOWS

```
O Y E S L W C U R S E T A G S
G F S R Q I C K U A I M Z A H
E F U E S N I E R A O N A C G
J I O B T D T S R D E G Y P T
U E H M S O Y T G V L I F E S
D L T A E W S N A O J O Y L G
G D A H R S I E R M T E G T N
M S P C L K H Y Q B E R I E I
E P Y R A U T C N A S O L C G
N O I T A G E R G N O C G A D
T S F O R T R E S S L K A E O
T S O L F T C W Z H C Z L P L
S E O A E N O I T N E T N O C
O S R N O R W E T E M P L E T
H S T D D M X H O L I E S T H
```

Bonus Trivia

What woman wore the first bridal veil mentioned in the Bible?

Rebekah (Genesis 24:65)

9

4
Writers in the Bible

BARUCH	HAMAN	JOSHUA
BISHLAM	HAND	JUDE
BRETHREN	HEZEKIAH	LUKE
DANIEL	HILKIAH	MORDECAI
DARIUS	HOSEA	MOSES
DAVID	ISAIAH	PAUL
ELIJAH	JEHU	PETER
EZEKIAL	JEREMIAH	PILATE
EZRA	JESUS	REHUM
GOD	JEZEBEL	STEPHANAS
HABAKKUK	JOHN	TERTIUS

```
H B D E P H H J J E Z E B E L
I H H K A A A M B I S H L A M
L M X U U I J I A C E D R O M
K N H L L A I R E H U M H Q D
I A C V D S L U H E J D A N S
A M U O M I E D A V I D B J A
H A R J E Z E K I A L D A U N
A H A B R E T H R E N H K D A
E Z B P I L A T E A Q A K E H
S L H J E S U S H H I I U L P
O O I J E R E M I A H K K E E
H S U I R A D D P E T E R I T
D D M O S E S A R Z E Z J N S
O T U T E R T I U S Q E C A S
G A U H S O J O H N V H U D W
```

Bonus Trivia

Where is the longest recorded prayer of Jesus?

John 17

5

Who or What Entered...

AMMONITES	LEPERS
CHRIST	LOT
DECEIVERS	LUKE
DEVILS	LUSTS
ENEMY	MOSES
FOREIGNERS	NOAH
HAMATH	NOE
HEATHEN	PRIEST
JEHU	REPROOF
JEREMIAH	SATAN
JESUS	SIN
JOSEPH	SPIES
KING	SPIRIT
LABAN	WISDOM
LAW	WOMEN

```
U M D S R E N G I E R O F L U
H T A M A H J B W F V R F E E
D J Y V X A L E E I Y L B P O
Q E K A Q L O Y R S S E M E N
J P V I S A T A N E P D M R Z
U H A I N W C Y S H M I O S D
D A Q P L G A I M P M I E M E
O O F U I S N M E E K G A S C
J N S P I R I T M S N A F H E
A E C N A B A L M O S E S S I
J E H Z S T S U L J N N C H V
E R P U P R I E S T E I A I E
S L N E H T A E H M D Q T D R
U P V F D F F O O R P E R E S
S C H R I S T W E K U L Q E S
```

Bonus Trivia

What was Paul's first sermon subject at Damascus, following his conversion?

He preached Christ. . .that he is the Son of God. (Acts 9:20)

6

Special Babies

ABEL	LEVI
ASHER	MANASSEH
BENJAMIN	MEPHIBOSHETH
DAN	MOSES
EPHRAIM	NAPHTALI
GAD	OBED
ISAAC	PEREZ
ISSACHAR	REUBEN
JACOB	SAMSON
JEDIDIAH	SAMUEL
JESUS	SETH
JOASH	SIMEON
JOHN THE BAPTIST	SOLOMON
JOSEPH	ZEBULUN
JUDAH	ZERAH

```
V N L H T E H S O B I H P E M
D U E A J C D R M P R M Y I S
A L U D P V E W S E A E H S U
N U M U D H D O U N P A Q A S
B B A J S E L B A H I N D A E
E E S A B O E S R D A T A C J
N Z H O M N S A I P E R E Z F
J K J O A E I D H S A M S O N
A V N J H M E T I M A N U H S
M B N L S J A S S I M E O N H
I G E E J L I G H J A C O B P
N P S L I I D T Z G A D G E E
J O H N T H E B A P T I S T S
M X Y P H S A O J L E V I D O
M R N I S S A C H A R E Z I J
```

Bonus Trivia

Who instigated mob action against Paul at
Ephesus?

7

Special Mothers, Daughters, & Sisters

ABIGAIL

ACHSAH

BATHSHEBA

BILHAH

DEBORAH

DINAH

EVE

HANNAH

HOGLAH

JEHOSHEBA

JOCHEBED

LEAH

MAHLAH

MARY

MIRIAM

NOAH

PUAH

RACHEL

RAHAB

REBEKAH

RUTH

SARAH

SHIPHRAH

TAMAR

TIRZAH

WIDOW OF NAIN

ZIBIAH

ZILPAH

ZIPPORAH

```
N H A R H P I H S B A H A R I
I H Z N M A B Z A H Q E E V H
Q H A I I A B I I E A P V A Y
H L A U L A I E L P L Z O E R
A S I K P P N R H H P N R T A
R H A A E B A F I S A O Z I M
O A B S G B N H O M O H R A T
B N E H V I E U D W Q H C A S
E N H U I T B R E M O H E S H
D A S N Z A D A B H S D A J M
D H H A I M K C A A A R I E A
I U T M B A I L H F A M J W H
N S A I I R G U C H R U T H L
A N B T A O N G O D B U C Q A
H X L E H C A R J O E E C W H
```

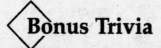

◇ Bonus Trivia

Who did Jesus refer to as "that fox"?

Herod (Luke 13:31-32)

8

Mothers in the Bible

ABI	JERUSHA
ADAH	LOIS
AHOLIBAMAH	MAACAH
ASENATH	MESHULLEMETH
ATARAH	MEZAHAB
ATHALIAH	MILCAH
AZUBAH	NAAMAH
EUNICE	NAOMI
HAGAR	SARAI
HAMUTAL	SERAH
HEPHZIBAH	SHUA
HERODIAS	TIMNA
JECOLIAH	ZEBUDAH
JEDIDAH	ZIBIAH
JEHOADDAN	ZILLAH

```
M L M V N J E R U S A L E M J
H A E J H A B I Z H P E H P E
A T S H S C H A L L I Z Q A R
M U H H A S A I D O R E H J U
A M U E M G H Y Q Y L O E U S
A A L H A R A T A O L H H B H
N H L M A J R R I I O A A A A
H H E J C O E S B A D H D H E
A T M I A O S A D U A I M A C
I A E M H A M D B Z D I J B I
L N T O D A A E E E L C O U N
O E H A H N Z M J C Z R F Z U
C S H N Y O Y S A N M I T A E
E A S A R A I H Z I B I A H I
J Z A T H A L I A H I B A P E
```

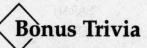

Bonus Trivia

Who shut the door of Noah's ark?

God (Genesis 7:16)

9

Couples in the Bible

ABRAHAM	JEZEBEL
ACHSAH	JOANNA
ADAM	JOSEPH
AHAB	LEAH
AHASUERUS	MARY
ANANIAS	MOSES
AQUILA	OTHNIEL
ASENATH	PRISCILLA
BATHSHEBA	RACHEL
BOAZ	RAHAB
CHUZA	REBEKAH
DAVID	RUTH
ESTHER	SALMON
EVE	SAPPHIRA
HAMAN	SARAH
ISAAC	ZERESH
JACOB	ZIPPORAH

```
S A P P H I R A B R A H A M Z
D A V I D H P E S O J H R H A
S A L M O N N A M A H A Y A O
B B A T H S H E B A H R Z N B
O V H A A L I U Q A A O Z N E
C L E I N H T O B M M P H A S
A Q R E B E K A H Z A P A O T
J W S A Z U H C E S D I R J H
A L L I C S I R P S A Z A E E
G I S A A C E R H T U R S N R
M O S E S S A S E N A T H C Z
R H A S H C A S J E Z E B E L
Q E C W X R A C H E L Q Z Z E
H V A H A S U E R U S B A H A
C E I V A N A N I A S N C L H
```

Bonus Trivia

What chapter in Isaiah's prophecy describes the sufferings of Christ?

Isaiah 53

10
Brothers in the Bible

ABEL	JACOB
ABINADAB	JOAB
ABISHAI	JOKSHAN
ABRAM	JONATHAN
ASAHEL	LAHMI
CAIN	MEDAN
DAVID	MIDIAN
ELIAB	NAHOR
ESAU	SAPH
GOLIATH	SETH
HARAN	SHAMMAH
ISAAC	SHIMEA
ISHBAK	SHUAH
ISHBIBENOB	SIPPAI
ISHBOSHETH	ZIMRAN
ISHMAEL	

```
Q H L V D A V I D H A R A N D
L Z E H T E H S O B H S I Z P
E I B O N E B I B H S I C M B
A S A D A H A H I S S H I E A
M A P Y R A N U P M E A X D D
H A K Y M M X N H Y H T G A A
S C V D I M B A A S S A H N N
I Q J E Z A A A I H I J L H I
L Q A G V H P B I N T K O Z B
E T C O R S A M A L C A L A A
H A O L S E E H I A E G N A B
A G B I S A O M I D I A N O M
S V R A Y R P N N A H S K O J
A L U T H A U H S I P P A I P
K A B H S I W Z P A B R A M Q
```

◇ **Bonus Trivia**

How many books of the Bible did John write?

Five

11

More Brothers in the Bible

ABDEEL	KEDEMAH
ABIDA	KENAZ
ASSHURIM	KORAH
DEDAN	LETUSHIM
DUMAH	LEUMMIM
ELDAAH	MASSA
ELIPHAZ	MIBSAM
EPHAH	MISHMA
EPHER	NAPHISH
GATAM	NEBAJOTH
HADAD	OMAR
HANOCH	REUEL
JAALAM	SHEBA
JETUR	TEMA
JEUSH	TEMAN
KEDAR	ZEPHO

```
E Y D K E M M F T C C R Z K A
B X T P I Z I M S K X U A E H
S G H B Z A S H A O Y T H D A
U A S H E N H D A T D E P E D
H A I A P E M T K A A J I M A
M Y H N H K A A E E D G L A D
B C P O O P S M L M D L E H H
M V A C A S R E I L A A E A E
W A N H H S E D E M Y N R R P
A M L U H D S T E D M O D R H
J B R A B L U A U D K U A U E
U I E A A S E M M L A M E L R
M C I H H J A U J W O N K L F
Y U X I S H U N E B A J O T H
Q V M M H S U E J R A D I B A
```

Bonus Trivia

Who was the first man mentioned in the Bible to preach from a pulpit?

Ezra (Nehemiah 8:4)

12

What's Burning?

ANGER	HOUSE
BELLOWS	JEALOUSY
BODY	LAKE
BONES	ODOURS
CAPTAINS	REEDS
CHAFF	ROLL
CHILDREN	RUBBISH
CITY	SACRIFICES
COALS	SONS
EARTH	TREE
ENEMIES	WEAPONS
FLESH	WICKED
GATES	WICKEDNESS
GRASS	WORK
HEART	WRATH

```
B O D Y A Z Y S U O L A E J V
Y T I C B I C A P T A I N S W
A N G E R H D C R E E D S F R
U C Q G A T E S S W O R K L A
C W M S O N S E E C E A L E T
H H C H A F F B N C A D A S H
I S S S Q Q S G O E H H K H H
L I W R G B I Q B B M U E T L
D B O U E S U O H H Q I R L L
R B L O X M S O E D W A E A O
E U L D V L O A Q M E G I S R
N R E O A S R W I C K E D L C
W U B O G T S N O P A E W M Y
S A C R I F I C E S G R A S S
E E R T W I C K E D N E S S R
```

◇ **Bonus Trivia**

What man owned a vineyard which was coveted by his king?

Naboth (1 Kings 21:2)

13

Now What's Burning?

ACHAN	JERUSALEM
AI	LAMP
BLOOD	MOUNTAIN
BRICK	OFFERING
BULLS	PALACE
BUSH	RAM
CHARIOTS	SHECHEM
DUNG	SHEEP
DUST	SODOM
FAT	STONES
GARMENT	TEMPLE
GOATS	WATER
GOMORRAH	WOOD
GROVES	ZIKLAG
INCENSE	ZIMRI
JERICHO	

```
O A K J K C I R B T R K W C I
F P E S O D O M S A B N A Y N
F V D O O L B U M U T I S S C
E J V A C G D E L E T G T E E
R E C X O Y C L M A N O O V N
I R M A G A S P Q C E M I O S
N U T O L N L C U H M O R R E
G S R A U E U J W A R R A G M
R A P Z I N S D E N A R H M E
B L J G I R T E I R G A C H H
G E H K A M E A N K I H P S C
W M K L L L R T I O M C D U E
M O H A F W K I A N T O H B H
J N M C A S R I V W O S C O S
L P I Q T U Q G Z W P E E H S
```

Bonus Trivia

What man made an effort to purchase the power of God with money?

Simon, the sorcerer (Acts 8)

14

Fathers of Kings

ABIJAH

AHAZ

AHAZIAH

AHIJAH

AMAZIAH

AMON

ASA

BAASHA

DAVID

ELAH

GADI

GINATH

HEROD

HEZEKIAH

JABESH

JEHOAHAZ

JEHOASH

JEHORAM

JEHOSHAPHAT

JEHU

JEROBOAM

JESSE

JOASH

JORAM

JOSIAH

JOTHAM

KISH

MANASSEH

MENAHEM

NEBAT

OMRI

REMALIAH

SOLOMON

```
R H T J H E S S A N A M W Z L
E J E H O S H A P H A T H V P
M N G U F O M J W H S J A X W
A E A H M E O A A D O K I H H
L B D R N R M I I S L L Z T A
I A I A A A K V I A O Z A A J
A T H M Z E A A H J M H H N I
H E S I Z D H S M N O S A I B
M T A E J J A A A K N A J G A
M H H M O A R M A O B O R E J
A Z A A B O B H A B K H M S S
H A S J H J A E E M C E G S H
T H A E I L E B S R O J K E S
O A J D E H A H I H O N F J I
J E H O A H A Z U R I D G A K
```

◇ Bonus Trivia

Who usurped authority in the church?

Diotrephes (3 John 9–10)

15
Judges & Oppressors

ABDON	JOTHAM
ABIMELECH	MESOPOTAMIA
AMMON	MIDIAN
BARAK	MOAB
CUSHAN	OREB
DEBORAH	OTHNIEL
EGLON	PHILISTINES
EHUD	SAMSON
ELI	SAMUEL
ELON	SHAMGAR
GIDEON	SISERA
IBZAN	TOLA
JABIN	ZALMUNNA
JAIR	ZEBAH
JEPHTHAH	ZEEB

```
B M E S O P O T A M I A Z S S
Z B T H N N S O T H N I E L R
A C A O A A D R C G I D E O N
L L L R M H B E R O N L B N P
M E O S A I T K B A N T E V H
U G O T C K H H I O D F R C I
N N A Z B I A D P U R A Y R L
N J A B I N I N A E G A E I I
A M M O N M Z R A M J A H A S
L E U M A S E B A H O A W J T
W N C E T S D H N Z S A E S I
P T H L I O S K E O E U B L N
O U H S N F O O L I L B C R E
D K M A H T O J O I O G A X S
A B I M E L E C H R T Q E H J
```

> ## Bonus Trivia

What famous rabbi was Paul's teacher?

Gamaliel (Acts 22:3)

16

Burial Places

AIJALON	JERUSALEM
BENJAMIN	KADESH
BETHEL	MAMRE
BETHLEHEM	MOAB
CAMON	PIRATHON
CAVE	POTTER'S FIELD
EPHRAIM	RAMAH
ESHTAOL	SAMARIA
FIELD OF BLOOD	SHAMIR
GARDEN	SHECHEM
GILEAD	TIRZAH
HEBRON	WILDERNESS
HOR	ZEBULUN
HOUSE	ZELAH
JABESH	ZORAH

```
I R Z M O K N O H T A R I P U
I Q O Q E M R X Z B P D M K E
T I R Z A H I L E H T E B N K
G H A G G D C N L K K J D Y D
K O H I M I J E A M N E O S L
A R J O J A L I H O G R O S E
D G A A M A E E M S Z U L E I
E B A I B R L A A E N S B N F
S S N R M E C O B D O A F R S
H A B A D S S U N R R L O E R
T M M E H E L H T E B E D D E
A A P A A U N R H R E M L L T
O R M T N T M I A R H P E I T
L I K Z Z D H A M A R W I W O
R A K C A V E E S U O H F P P
```

⬦ **Bonus Trivia**

What sexual sin did Paul see as the result of not worshipping the true God?

Homosexuality (Romans 1:26–27)

17

Killed

ABEL	JONATHAN
ABINADAB	JOSIAH
ABNER	LAHMI
ABSALOM	MALCHISHUA
ACHAN	NABOTH
AHAB	RECHAB
AMASA	SAPH
AMNON	SAUL
ASAHEL	SHEBA
ATHALIAH	SHOPHACH
BAANAH	SIPPAI
GOLIATH	STEPHEN
ISHBOSHETH	TIBNI
JAMES	UZZAH
JESUS	ZIMRI
JEZEBEL	

```
F O R D T U L H C A H P O H S
M I E U T I B N I A P P I S L
U F N W M A B S A L O M L N E
U Z B H A S Z A B I N A D A B
A Z A M E G S I S S A B L B E
B L Z M Y U H S U A H E M O Z
E W A A S N R H S C T H A T E
L J Q E H E E B A H A S S H J
A I J H A H C O U A N S A P H
S R S L I P H S L N O W M Z W
A M A D S E A H W J J O A H D
H I M A O T B E H L E A H A B
E Z N A J S D T B A A N A H X
L G O L I A T H A L I A H O C
X Q N I A U H S I H C L A M U
```

◇ **Bonus Trivia**

How old was Abraham when Isaac was born?

100 (Genesis 21:5)

18

Feeble & Weak . . .

BODY	JEWS
BROTHER	KNEES
CATTLE	LAW
CONSCIENCE	NATIONS
CRUCIFIED	PAUL
DAMASCUS	PENINNAH
DAVID	PEOPLE
FAITH	PRESENCE
FLESH	REMNANT
HANDS	SAMSON
HEART	STRENGTH
HOUSE OF SAUL	THINGS
INFIRMITIES	VESSEL
ISHBOSHETH	WATER
ISRAEL	WIFE

H	A	N	N	I	N	E	P	D	S	S	E	E	N	K
Q	D	H	E	A	R	T	E	T	F	J	U	G	E	M
K	R	E	R	M	A	I	R	R	E	F	Z	C	S	E
L	E	O	F	E	F	E	Z	W	H	L	N	U	F	L
U	H	T	H	I	N	G	S	T	O	E	C	S	U	S
A	T	V	C	G	W	N	E	Z	S	S	Z	A	C	E
P	O	U	T	X	A	H	Z	E	A	H	S	M	R	I
D	R	H	Q	T	S	P	R	M	I	F	Z	S	E	T
C	B	X	I	O	E	P	A	S	O	H	H	O	M	I
Y	D	O	B	O	E	D	R	E	T	A	W	N	N	M
R	N	H	P	L	A	A	S	W	N	F	Z	J	A	R
S	S	L	T	V	E	U	A	D	K	C	V	E	N	I
I	E	T	I	L	O	L	S	F	A	I	T	H	T	F
O	A	D	M	H	V	E	S	S	E	L	E	U	R	N
C	C	O	N	S	C	I	E	N	C	E	L	Y	P	I

◇ Bonus Trivia

Where were the disciples first called Christians?

Antioch (Acts 11:26)

19

Strong

ANGEL	KING
BRICK KILN	KINGDOM
CONFIDENCE	LOINS
CONSOLATION	MEAT
CRYING	OAKS
DEATH	ONE
DELUSION	PEOPLE
FACE	POWER
FAITH	REASONS
FOREHEAD	RODS
FOUNDATIONS	STAFF
GARRISONS	SWORD
GOD	TREE
GRACE	VOICE
HORSES	WATCH
IRON	WRATH

```
G S W R A T H E V R O D S L O
A P F G R C O N F I D E N C E
R D H K E E B U O N E D W S U
R C B C I C A M E A T A K T T
I S O R T N A S H L I E T A T
S N D N I A G F O R I H R F V
O O A E S C W P O N P E E F K
N I K B L O K N E N S R E C I
S T F D D U L K S O U O P R N
H A A E H R S A I E P F O Y G
O D I A A T O I T L C L W I D
R N T O G N A W O I N A E N O
S U H O A Z G E S N O S R G M
E O D I Q K N E D D C N B G C
S F L O I N S Z L B V O I C E
```

Bonus Trivia

How old was Methuselah when he died?

969 (Genesis 5:27)

20

Strong # 2

AMMON	LION
ARM	LORD
BRASS	MAN
BULLS	MEN
CALEB	MOUNTAIN
CHARIOTS	NATIONS
CITIES	OXEN
CONSPIRACY	PAIN
DRINK	PLACE
DWELLING	REDEEMER
ENEMY	REFUGE
HABITATION	ROCK
HAND	TOWER
HOLDS	TYRE
ISRAEL	WIND
ISSACHAR	WINE
JOSHUA	

```
R Q N M T S G N D N I W N B T
E A G N I L L E W D H O D U C
M N S T N L E A R S I R C H E
E I E L O U O N L T I O A G F
E A I C M B K I A N N R U N A
D P T A M K O T K S I F E R N
E Q I L A N I J P O E M M U A
R Y C E W B G I T R R U T D T
A T O B A O R S E N E M Y V I
U O V H H A N D W L O R D T O
H W B S C C H C Y E C A L P N
S E X Y E E R A H C A S S I S
O R Y P U S D L O H B R A S S
J N E X O E N I W T E T Y R E
N I A T N U O M P K C O R G N
```

⬧ **Bonus Trivia**

What strange phenomenon accompanied the plague of hail in Egypt?

Fire that ran along the ground (Exodus 9:23)

21

Sacrifice (To)

ABOMINATION

BAAL

BAALIM

BLIND

BROKEN SPIRIT

BULLS

BURNT

CONTRITE HEART

DAGON

DEVILS

FAT

FATLINGS

FIRE

FLESH

GOATS

GOD

IDOLS

INCENSE

JESUS

JOY

LAMB

LORD

MOLECH

NET

OFFERINGS

OXEN

PEACE

PRAISE

RIGHTEOUSNESS

SHEEP

THANKSGIVING

```
N D N I L B M X F P B G T N C
L G O A T S R A X A N N O B O
S J O Y U E T E A I R I V B N
S S I S S L C L V U T F R N T
H K E I I A I I B A B O F T R
E J A N E M G N N M K A M O I
E R G P S S U I A E T H Y F T
P S C R K U M L N D S J A F E
O X E N S O O S H L A D C E H
R P A L B M P E O S E G S R E
K H L A O I G D T V E N O I A
T U N L R B I O I H E L L N R
B I E I A L Q L D C G T F G T
D C T A J P S G N K Y I E S G
H Z L O R D G I E R I F R N K
```

◁ **Bonus Trivia**

How many soldiers were engaged in the
dark deed of crucifying Jesus?

Four (John 19:23)

45

22

Keepers

ALTAR	HOME
ARK	HOUSE
BROTHERS	LAW
CARRIAGE	MEMORY
CHARGE	PRISON
COMMANDMENTS	SAYINGS
COMPANY	SHEEP
DOOR	SILENCE
ENTRY	UNITY
FEET	VINEYARDS
FIELDS	WALLS
FOREST	WARDROBE
GATE	WATCH
GATES	WOMEN
HEAD	YOURSELF

```
K T W A L L S M E M O R Y Q R
U C S C O M M A N D M E N T S
N O T E E F G A T E S S P P C
I M Z O R O S D R A Y E N I V
T P C S W O L H T D P E W P K
Y A W G Y B F A P A X G A R K
Z N A N O R C E W Z E A N C Y
R Y R I U O H S T F K I E R N
O P D Y R T A W C A D R C A O
O E R A S H R D A F G R N T S
D E O S E E G T A T A A E L I
R H B X L R E E M E C C L A R
Z S E B F S M K L J H H I G P
Y R T N E O N E M O W L S T G
E S U O H B S D L E I F S J V
```

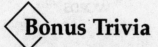

Bonus Trivia

What prophet was married to a prophetess?

Isaiah (Isaiah 8:3)

23

Keepers # 2

ANGER	PASSOVER
COURTS	PATHS
COVENANT	PAUL
DISCRETION	PEACE
EDEN	PRECEPTS
FEAST	RANK
FLOCK	SABBATH
HEART	SOUL
HOLINESS	STATUTES
JUDGMENT	TESTIMONY
KNOWLEDGE	TONGUE
LIFE	TRADITION
MYSELF	TREE
OATH	WISDOM
ORDINANCE	WORDS

```
T E C N A N I D R O H S D H T
E C K C S D R O W Q O U F O T
S E O N O O N N F U K N L L N
T L F V O U S O L W X E O I E
I S F I E W R H I M N D C N M
M S E J L N L T T T O E K E G
O K N T I V A E S A I D H S D
N R N M U T S N D H P D S S U
Y E M A P T S A T G E Q A I J
M V Y O R P A A B J E A M R W
Y O S Z A Q D T E B H C R U T
E S E U G N O T S F A T A T G
E S L S T P E C E R P T A E E
R A F R A F L R E G N A H O P
T P N O I T E R C S I D W A C
```

Bonus Trivia

What does Satan masquerade as in the present world?

An angel of light (2 Corinthians 11:14)

24

Husbands in the Bible

ABRAHAM	JOSEPH
ADAM	JUDAH
BOAZ	LOT
CAIN	MACHIR
ELIMELECH	MANOAH
ELKANAH	MOSES
ER	NABAL
ESAU	NAHOR
GOD	NOAH
HAM	ONAN
HOSEA	PALTIEL
ISAAC	PETER
ISHMAEL	SAMSON
JACOB	SETH
JAPHETH	SHEM
JOB	URIAH

```
J Q N A N O V C H O H U I J Y
N E R O H A N A C P Y R C U K
I M A C H I R A E C J I A D R
H A O N S Z J S L B A A I A F
A M A K I R O I E O P H N H I
B O C A J J Z T M J H E T O L
H S R L G K H J I V E R T P I
O E D I E G R D L Q T H H E V
S S V L N A Z F E M H A L H R
E R Z U A O M A A B M N E A F
A R A C M B S H O X G A I O Q
S S G H R E A M S B O K T N W
E E T J P R H N A I D L L A M
A E R K B D L S X S Q E A M A
S F I A G F U V A D A M P E H
```

◇ Bonus Trivia

What color was the cloth draped over the ark of the covenant?

Blue (Numbers 4:6)

25

More Husbands in the Bible

AARON	JARHA
ABISHUR	LABAN
ADRIEL	LAMECH
AHAB	LAPIDOTH
AMRAM	LEVI
ANAH	MAHLON
BEERI	NAAMAN
CALEB	NAHOR
CHUZA	NATHAN
DAVID	OTHNIEL
ELI	PHINEHAS
GIDEON	SAUL
GILEAD	SHUAH
HARAN	TERAH
HEBER	ZIBEON
HEZRON	

```
H W K L B E E R I D D I V A D
A O T A U H P H I N E H A S N
U A H E E A I X A N O L H A M
H A L Z I D S A H A R A N F A
S I R A F A Z L N N R C C N U
G O I R P U E E O S U S A W Q
N N C Y H I P P R J H H L F V
Z I E C R I D Y A F S C E H N
N P N D H A V O A X I K B A O
H O A A M C J E T L B X T R T
E J E R A A E N L H A H E O H
B Z A D R M F M U U A B R H N
E M K H I B A Q A N K O A A I
R G A K G G T N B L V U H N E
D N O E B I Z R G I L E A D L
```

Bonus Trivia

Is there a woman in the Bible named Noah?

Yes (Numbers 26:33)

26

Graves & Sepulchres (of)

ABNER	JOSEPH
ABRAHAM	JOSIAH
AHAZIAH	KINGS
AMON	KISH
ARMONI	LAZARUS
ASAHEL	LEAH
BONES	MEPHIBOSHETH
ELISHA	MOSES
FATHERS	PROPHET
GIDEON	RACHEL
ISAAC	REBEKAH
JACOB	RIGHTEOUS
JESUS	SARAH
JOASH	SAUL
JONATHAN	THROAT

```
R Y T A O R H T Q G V Z M E C
N E G M Q O M R J N B B A S I
O L Z L E A H M Y O C O H S H
E I N R S P Q O N M R C A U B
D S B A E E H E M A J A R R M
I H Y T H B S I J A C J B A J
G A Y P J T E O B O B N A Z O
X I C I R E A K M O A N I A S
R Z H J N O S N A Z S S E L E
K A G T K O P U O H Y H H R P
I H C I J H M H S J W I E K H
S A N H A T S R E H T A F T Y
H G N R E W L Q A T L U A S H
S B A T X L R I G H T E O U S
A S A H E L J O S I A H X G N
```

Bonus Trivia

What was the penalty for kidnapping in the Old Testament?

Death (Exodus 21:16)

27

Who Begat Whom?

ALMODAD	MEHUJAEL
ARPHAXAD	METHUSAEL
CAINAN	METHUSELAH
CANAAN	MIZRAIM
EBER	NAHOR
ENOCH	NIMROD
ENOS	NOAH
HAM	PELEG
IRAD	REU
JAPHETH	SALAH
JARED	SERUG
JOKTAN	SHELEPH
LAMECH	SHEM
LUDIM	SIDON
MAHALALEEL	TERAH

```
N O D I S Q F S H E M M D S Z
U K M S J O K T A N I E O A V
V R E A D B A B O D Z H R L H
V E T S R J C M R X R U M A A
E U H S H P A O F E A J I H O
N L U E C L H P C M I A N V N
O E S R O A U A H H M E H L H
S E E U N E I D X E G L P E C
U L L G E N T G I A T Q E A E
C A A I A F E M E M D H L S M
V L H N D E R A J L A D E U A
N A A N A C A V A V E H H H L
O H S B G L H O M C H P S T O
Q A D A L M O D A D F X F E T
P M R E B E Z D A R I G A M K
```

◇ Bonus Trivia

What book of the Bible records the shortest prayer?

Matthew (14:30) Lord, save me!

28
Whom Begat Whom? # 2

ABRAM	JORAM
AMINADAB	JOSEPH
AMRAM	JUDAH
ASHER	KOHATH
BENJAMIN	LEVI
BOAZ	LOT
DAN	MACHIR
DAVID	MANASSEH
DEDAN	NAASSON
EPHRAIM	NAPHTALI
GAD	OBED
GILEAD	REBEKAH
HARAN	REUBEN
ISAAC	SALMON
ISSACHAR	SHEBA
JACOB	SIMEON
JESSE	ZEBULUN
JOKSHAN	

```
Z I A M R A M A C H I R S K D
N T S M I A R H P E B K A H E
U N E S D I V A D V O O L E D
L I A N A M H R E E C H M S A
U R G H T C O A X S A A O S N
B E N M S O H N K S J T N A I
E H I A H K L A P E A H G N M
Z S V R A C O T R J B G G A A
U A E B W O A J T E E E A M J
Z I L A T H P A N B H V R D N
A D A E L I G O S D S O D Y E
O D E B O N A D S I M E O N B
B A D A N I M A M A R O J U W
X L Z W H P E S O J H A D U J
N E B U E R Q N O S S A A N Q
```

Bonus Trivia

What book tells us that God makes weight for the winds? (a fact that was not scientifically established until the 17th century by Pascal)

The book of Job (28:25)

29
Teachings of Proverbs

ATTAIN	ORNAMENT
COUNSEL	PEACE
DELIGHT	PERCEIVE
DWELL	POUR
ENIGMA	PRUDENCE
FEAR	REBUKE
GRACE	RECEIVE
GUARD	REPROOF
HAPPY	RIDDLES
HEALTH	SAFELY
HONOUR	SHIELD
JUSTICE	SUBTLETY
KNOWN	TRUST
LEARNING	WISDOM
LIFE	WORDS
LORD	

```
E K N O W N S E L D D I R N E
E N D E R E P R O O F Y I K J
I V I R E D L E I H S A U U N
R T I G O F Q O G N T B S B G
L E R E M L I I R T E T N N R
Y W C R C A O L A R I T I U R
P L I E A R O S C C S N O P U
Y C E S I E E C E U R N E U O
T T R F D V F P R A O I K Q P
E L Y W A O E T E H C O J J V
L W O R D S M L H T L A E H N
T H D W E L L P R U D E N C E
B E C A E P T N E M A N R O C
U A S D R A U G L E S N U O C
S H A P P Y T H G I L E D Z S
```

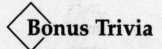

30

Five in the Bible

BARLEY	MONTHS
BARS	OXEN
BASES	PIECES
BRETHREN	PORCHES
CITIES	POUNDS
CUBITS	RAMS
DAYS	SHEEP
GOATS	SHEKELS
GOLDEN	SINGING
HUNDRED	SOCKETS
HUSBANDS	SONS
KINGS	STONES
LAMBS	TALENTS
LOAVES	THOUSAND
LORDS	TIMES
MEASURES	TREES
MEN	WORDS
MICE	YEARS

```
S M M B P R Y G K I N G S B T
T D E L A S T O N E S H A R S
S H N A I R L O A V E S E T C
D S O U S O L W E K E E E U M
N D H U O U A E E S S K B O T
A R S E S P R L Y D C I N G A
B O O B E A S E R O T T O N L
S W N V M P N O S S H L N I E
U C S S C L D S S D E E G N
H C I T I E S Y L E R Y X N T
F T A A D E E A N H M A O I S
T O F E C A M P T P K I B S H
G I C E R B Y E Z A B E T C I
J I I S S I R S H U N D R E D
M P N M Y B W S E H C R O P D
```

Bonus Trivia

Who is the first female singer mentioned in the Bible?

Miriam (Exodus 15:21)

31

That Woman

AMEN	GORE
AMONG	HEBREW
BARE	HID
BEAR	ISSUE
BEAUTIFUL	KILL
BEGUILED	MADE
CAST	MARRIED
CONCEIVED	OATH
CURSE	SAW
DAWNING	SLEW
DEFILED	STRANGE
DELICATE	TOOK
DIVORCED	VALLEY
DRINK	VOW
ENMITY	WEAR
FAIR	WHOM

```
I T B E F O D E C R O V I D L
S D W E D W K X F K Q H T A O
S T Y F A A H H R V O D J W H
U M S Z D U M O O I D O J E Y
E L A A R E T W M G A K T R G
M D S R C O L I Q D N F E B G
B V A T R E D I F E R O G E D
R E W B R I N E C U P I M H E
A D G T A A E M V A L J N A L
E A H U Y E N D I I T P X K I
W W W E I E R G K T E E O U F
A N H S N L L A E I Y C Z A E
R I L R O E E L B L L W N T D
D N V U I V M D A W E L S O M
N G R C J N S A S V B E A R C
```

◇ **Bonus Trivia**

What prophet's word caused the Syrian
soldiers to be struck blind?

Elisha's (2 Kings 6:18–23)

32

That Woman # 2

ABODE

ALIVE

ANGRY

BARREN

BELOVED

BORN

CLOTHED

DECEIVED

DIED

EVIL

FAIR

FEARING

FLED

FOOLISH

FORGET

FREE

GRACIOUS

GREEK

LAIN

LAY

LEARN

ODIOUS

PANGS

PRAY

RETURNED

SIT

SLAIN

SORROWFUL

SPAKE

TEKOA

TRAVAIL

VIRTUOUS

WHORISH

WICKED

WIDOW

WISE

YOUNG

```
O E O A Z F L T E K O A G F V
D K W Q L I A V A R T R E V D
E A W K V I B I F A A A I E D
K P H E E A V O R C R R V X E
C S O E U D R E I I T O B Y C
I F R R I G C O N U L K O R E
W L I G E L U G O E N D T G I
O E S T O S F U B I I R B N V
D D H T P O S Q L O E E O A E
I K H F O S P E U S R S Z B D
W E R L L A A S I Y A R P A D
D E I A N R X W N E R R A B I
E S I G N U O Y H K L A Y O E
H N S O R R O W F U L T O D D
C C O S I T C D E N R U T E R
```

Bonus Trivia

How many times does Eve's name appear in the New Testament?

Twice (2 Corinthians 11:3; 1 Timothy 2:13)

33

It's That Time

ALTAR	MOCKED
BEFORE	MUCH
BLESSED	OBSERVE
BLOOD	OTHER
BOWED	PAST
CAMP	PLAGUES
CHILD	PURIFIED
CITY	SEVEN
DAN	SINS
DAVID	SMITTEN
FINGER	SUPPLANTED
GROUND	TEN
KEEP	THOUSAND
LEPROSY	TWO
MANNER	WAGES
MANY	YEAR

```
Y Y B F S E V E N F K E E P I
P U R I F I E D B Q X S T N N
W R R A E Y A M Y P B E Y N E
Q L G E V R E S B O S G N A T
S E U G A L P Q D B S A A D T
Z T W P M A C N P U C W M D I
D E W O B A A Q P B M I A J M
Y S D O T S L P T A L V T O S
L H N T U H L T N R I O C Y D
E Q T O T A E N A D E K O E Q
P L H S N Y E R N R E G S D C
R T A T W R M U O D H S N H N
O P E G M U O F J N E T I I T
S D F F C R E J D L N L E Y F
Y Z Q H G B D K B V D S I N S
```

◇ **Bonus Trivia**

For what strange offense was a prophet
killed by a lion?

He refused the request of another prophet
to hit him. (1 Kings 20:35–36)

34

It's That Time # 2

ADJURE

ALL

ANCIENT

APPOINTED

BETTER

CHANGE

DIPPED

DUE

FIVE

FOUR

FULNESS

GENTILES

JOASH

JORDAN

LAST

MANIFESTED

MANY

MONTHS

OLD

PASS

PETITION

RECEIVED

REFRESHING

RESTITUTION

SEASONS

SHEW

SIGNS

SIX

SNEEZED

STABILITY

SUNDRY

TROUBLE

TRUST

WASH

```
F U L N E S S O G Q M D M V N
A S T R O U B L E O U G G U O
X U N E V I F D N E E L G S I
S N M G B E T T E R L E S R T
N D A S I X H S U A N A U M U
E R N I Y S G J H T P O J D T
E Y I X T T D S I E F C O E I
Z C F G I A A L W K W C R V T
E H E I L W E D E P P I D I S
D A S J I S E A S O N S A E E
A N T O B T N E I C N A N C R
T G E A A Y A P P O I N T E D
S E D S T N O I T I T E P R J
A A N H S T R U S T Y N A M W
L R E F R E S H I N G L H O G
```

◇ **Bonus Trivia**

What was the first city called?

Enoch, named after Cain's son (Genesis 4:17)

35
What About Wood?

ALTAR	OFFERING
ARK	ORDER
BARS	PEOPLE
BRASS	PLACE
BRING	PULPIT
BURNT	ROTTEN
CART	ROUND
CARVING	SERVE
CEDAR	SHITTIM
CHARIOT	SOLD
COUNTRY	STAVES
DEVOURED	STONES
FIR	TABLE
FIRE	THYINE
GATHER	TREES
HEW	VESSEL
IDOLS	WEAPON
KINDLE	YOKES

```
P K Q N E T T O R T B A R S T
C C O U N T R Y O R G S R P R
M I T T I H S I G N I T O U A
E Y A S S A R B I N H F W L C
M B L U E A G V Q Y I E R P D
G D T E H V R R I E A R F I H
A E A C C A A N A P L Q B T E
T V R D C A E T O D V D O L W
H O T N J B L N S K E E N H Y
E U R U A P K P O N S C Q I O
R R E O L S E R V E S E S Z K
V E E R E D R O B L E R L W E
S D S T N R U B P W L I O P S
F E A R K B T A B L E F D A G
S E N O T S Z O F F E R I N G
```

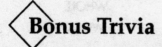

Bonus Trivia

Who built Nineveh?

Asshur (Genesis 10:11)

36
Till Who, What, or When

ACCOMPLISH	MATTER
AFTER	MIRIAM
ASHAMED	MOON
BLOOD	MORNING
COME	MOSES
CONSUMED	PEOPLE
DAY	REMEDY
DESTROYED	ROLL
DIE	SHELAH
DRAWN	STARS
FILL	STOOD
FIND	STRONG
GONE	SUN
GROUND	SWALLOW
KNOW	WHOLE
LAND	WORK

```
G R O U N D P M Z C O M E D C
P D K Q H S I L P M O C C A M
H A E Y S R J P R E M E D Y A
N X S S I W D O O L B N O O M
O Y U A T M A N N B O D V J R
S G M H H R K L T F I L L T D
E N K D P A O R L E H B Y E C
S I L U E D L Y O O X A M S O
O N O V O U A E E W W A T T N
M R Q E P S E Y H D H A I R S
K O D L L D N R H S R D E O U
N M E O E S O N A S N T N N M
O J M H O L G U C A T N D G E
W W E W L T F S L A D N I F D
R E T F A D S O M N W A R D Q
```

Bonus Trivia

What was the name of Timothy's grandmother?

Lois (2 Timothy 1:5)

37

Till Who, What, or When # 2

AFTERWARDS	JOB
BURIERS	LEFT
CAST	LORD
CAUSED	MAN
CHANGE	MIGHT
DART	NOW
DIG	PERFORMED
DRUNKEN	PLACE
ENDED	PLEASE
ENOUGH	SCATTERED
ESTABLISH	SEE
FIND	SET
GOING	SEVEN
HAIRS	SUBMIT
HEAVEN	WINE
INIQUITY	WINGS

```
T M T G S G N I W C P C X L P
R E H H E E H V A P U O O M A
A N G C S A C S L E K R S F H
D D I V I I T A M X D W T G K
I E M R D Q L A L D J E I E W
L D S Q T E N B E P R D S H S
D N I F X B M S A W G A T G S
C B H H G S U R A T E M I U C
P U A E G A W R O L S E M O A
Q R R A C O D O P F E E B N T
A I T V R S I Z N S R P U E T
U E N E V E S N W I N E S C E
D R U N K E N Q G B T A P Z R
I S Q B O J C H A N G E K S E
Y L E F T X I N I Q U I T Y D
```

Bonus Trivia

What is it that you see every time you go to church, which is only mentioned once in the Bible?

Pulpit (Nehemiah 8:4)

77

38

Till Who, What, or When # 3

ACKNOWLEDGE	PAID
BEAST	PAY
BREAK	PLAGUES
BROUGHT	SAY
DENIED	SEALED
DEPART	SEE
EATEN	SEED
END	SEND
ENEMIES	SON
EVENING	STONE
FULFILLED	TARRY
INDIGNATION	THOUSAND
KILLED	THREE
KING	THRONE
KINGDOM	TIME
MORROW	UNITY

```
N E T H O U S A N D S E N D U
D S E I M E N E D E L A E S K
S E O F N M K I N G D O M J I
Y E L X E Z S M H I U E H C L
L T U L E G T R A P E D G W L
Q D I G I N D P Y S U B N G E
Q E E N A F D E C A A W I V D
T E E I U L L V L S P Y N B B
H S S K Y C P U T W D X E R E
R T H R O N E O F M O J V E A
E I N D I G N A T I O N E A S
E W J H D E I N E D H R K K T
K G L S O N Z Y R R A T R C R
J X T H G U O R B Z G H Y O A
G E A T E N W R P T I M E G W
```

◇ Bonus Trivia

How many books of the Bible end with a question?

Two—Jonah and Nahum!

39

Books of History & Prophecy in the Bible

ACTS	JUDGES
AMOS	KINGS
CHRONICLES	LAMENTATIONS
ESTHER	LUKE
EXODUS	MARK
EZEKIAL	MATTHEW
EZRA	MICAH
GENESIS	NAHUM
HABAKKUK	NEHEMIAH
HAGGAI	OBADIAH
HOSEA	REVELATION
ISAIAH	RUTH
JEREMIAH	SAMUEL
JOHN	ZECHARIAH
JONAH	ZEPHANIAH
JOSHUA	

```
S I S E N E G H A I D A B O J
H A I N A H P E Z Q A N S S O
J E H I S A I A H F E G D O N
O S A A C T S C R H N L G M A
S O B B L H M W E I A R I A H
H H A E U C T M K M C Z N H H
U H K S K J I U E H J O A M Q
A A K T E A V N R E I I A W Q
M C U H H G T O R T R T S L S
U I K E Q A N E A A T E A A M
H M N R T I M L H H G I M A V
A A F I C I E C E D K U R J N
N U O L A V E W U E E K K W H
S N E H E Z Y J Z L S L E E O
S S A R Z E B E E X O D U S J
```

Bonus Trivia

What man paid his fare to a certain place, but never arrived?

Jonah (Jonah 1:3–15)

40
Rivers in Bible Lands

ABANA	LITANI
ARAXES	LOIRE
BESOR	MEJARKON
CYRUS	NILE
DANUBE	ORONTES
DIYALA	PHARPAR
DNIEPER	PO
DNIESTER	RHINE
DOURO	RHONE
EUPHRATES	SANGARIUS
HALYS	TAGUS
HERMUS	TIGRIS
JABBOK	UZAN
JORDAN	VISTULA
KARUN	VOLGA
KISHON	YARMUK
LEONTES	ZARQA

```
Z C K U M R A Y R E P E I N D
A Y T N N E E N O H R P C K H
R E A O U H E R M U S O N W A
Q N G K R A P R A H P I I R D
A I U R A A G L O V L N A A S
L H S A K U Z A N E A X N S E
U R L J A B B O K T E U P U T
T Z E E T I G R I S B N R I A
S F R M H I R L X E J E E R R
I R I V I U Q L A D U G T A H
V H O B E S O R O N T E S G P
M A L Q A B A N A R Y S E N U
B L E O N T E S G P U V I A E
C Y R U S A L A Y I D O N S C
R S E K I S H O N J O R D A N
```

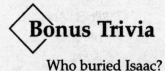

Bonus Trivia

Who buried Isaac?

Jacob and Esau (Genesis 35:29)

83

41

Lakes, Seas, Etc. in Bible Lands

ADRIATIC	ISRAEL
AEGEAN	MARMARA
AQABA	MAWJIB
ARISH	PERSIAN
ATLANTIC	PLAIN
BESOR	QUALJAFR
BITTER	RED
BLACK	SERPENTS
CASPIAN	SEVAN
DEAD	SHEEP
ENROGEL	SILOAM
GALILEE	TOWERS
GIHON	TUZ
GREAT	TYRRHENIAN
HASA	UPPER
HULA	VAN
IONIAN	

T	Y	R	R	H	E	N	I	A	N	D	H	N	R	E
S	E	R	P	E	N	T	S	O	S	S	A	F	N	T
C	A	S	P	I	A	N	H	R	I	I	A	R	H	A
L	H	R	Q	X	A	I	E	R	S	J	O	N	A	E
I	U	E	H	W	G	W	A	R	L	G	U	N	S	R
U	L	P	J	E	O	T	E	A	E	E	A	U	A	G
L	A	P	R	T	P	P	U	L	F	V	X	E	P	S
P	E	U	E	O	P	Q	P	Z	E	O	G	L	A	I
G	O	A	D	E	I	Y	K	S	B	E	A	B	R	L
L	A	W	R	O	H	C	I	T	A	I	R	D	A	O
F	I	L	N	S	A	S	D	N	N	C	M	S	M	A
H	O	I	I	L	I	E	Q	R	O	S	E	B	R	M
D	A	H	B	L	A	C	I	T	N	A	L	T	A	I
N	F	I	W	D	E	B	I	T	T	E	R	E	M	D
M	A	W	J	I	B	E	M	T	A	Q	A	B	A	M

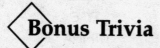

◇ Bonus Trivia

Who sent spies to watch Jesus?

The chief priests and scribes (Luke 20:19–20)

85

42

Cities with Waterfronts in Bible Lands

ACCHO	LYDDA
ALEXANDRIA	MAGDALA
ASSOS	MILETUS
BETHSAIDA	MYRA
BYLBOS	PAPHOS
CARTHAGE	PATARA
CENCHREA	PERGA
CORINTH	PTOLEMAIS
DELPHI	SALAMIS
DOR	SELEUCIA
GENNESARET	SIDON
ISSUS	TROAS
JOPPA	TYRE
LAODICEA	UTHINA
LASEA	

```
E G A H T R A C O H C C A T P
T L G G I A F I L Y D D A T H
P S L B S R Y C C G K E O N M
A A H E S Y I A S U R L L O A
T L P T U M L O T H E R A D G
A E S H S N S Z C M E L S I D
R X I S O S X N A R S L E S A
A A M A A S E I Y L Y X A S L
E N A I H C S T S A O R T Q A
S D L D G B J D M I L E T U S
U R A A Y O E A E C I D O A L
C I S L P L X H A N I H T U E
A A B P P G E N N E S A R E T
Y O A H S D A R O D A G R E P
S I I H P H T N I R O C I W M
```

43

Cities with Waterfronts in Bible Lands #2

ACHZIB	HAMATH
AHLAB	HAZOR
ARVAD	JERICHO
ASHKELON	KADESH
AVARIS	KNOSSUS
BEEROTH	LAISH
BEERSHEBA	MEROM
BETHSHAN	NINEVAH
BUSIRUS	RABBAH
CALAH	RAMESES
DAN	REHOB
EDREI	SIPPAR
EGLON	TANIS
ENGEDI	TIRZAH
GATH	TOB
GILGAL	ZARETAN
GOZAN	ZOAN

```
D R E H O B K R M E R O M B W
A I D K N L O O H C I R E J T
V M D O D Z I Y A H L A B R S
R Z L E A A B U S I R U S B E
A G O H G H N S T O B W I W S
E A W A K N B G I I M Z H A E
B T X Z N B E I R R H J A S M
E H X R O E E L S C A R B H A
T E R I S E R G A I P V B K R
H H A T S R O A D I N X A E N
S S P E U S T L C T S A R L A
H E P D S H H T A M A H T O Z
A D I R E E Z A R E T A N N O
N A S E T B H A V E N I N E G
A K C I J A U H A L A C P O Y
```

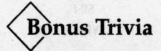

Bonus Trivia

What queen of Israel practiced witchcraft?

Jezebel (2 Kings 9:22)

89

44
Islands, Deserts, & Valleys in Bible Land

ARABAH	KIDRON
ARABIAN	MALTA
BALEARIC	MELITA
BEKAA	MITYLENE
CAPHTOR	PARAN
CENTRAL	PATMOS
CHIOS	RHODES
CLAUDA	SAHARA
CNIDUS	SAMOS
CORCYRA	SAMOTHRACE
COS	SARDINIA
CRETE	SHUR
CYPRUS	SICILY
EUBOEA	SIN
HINNOM	SYRIAN
IADANNA	

```
A S E D O H R Q B E B E K A A
R N E U B O E A T A R A H A S
Y L C O S Y W E O Q S R P R U
C K U Y N Y R S H U R A A A S
R I I S P C R M O R U B R B R
O S A D A R C I I I J A A I O
C S A D R R U P A T H H N A T
T J M M A O D S A N Y C O N H
Y W A M O N N I H T E L O I P
R S T T M T N S N N M S E D A
O U L Q E Y H A T I O O E N C
P D A Q L Y Z R H M A B S R E
O I M B I J A S A C L A U D A
E N A X T L S S I C I L Y P X
N C I R A E L A B N E Z Z H K
```

Bonus Trivia

What happens to the sea in the world to come?

It does not exist. (Revelation 21:1)

45
Archaeological Sites of Bible Lands

ABILA	HOMS
ABYDOS	IMAR
BADRA	ISINBETHEL
CAPERNAUM	JARMO
DAN	JEBUS
DELPHI	JERUSALEM
DER	KADESH
DOTHAN	KANAH
EBLA	KISH
ENGEDI	LUXOR
ERIDU	MARI
GADARA	MASADA
GAZA	NABLUS
GIBEON	NIMRUD
HAMATH	SIPPAR
HARAN	

```
I C J B C R M E L A S U R E J
E B L A L A N A D R M Y E I S
X T Y I C E P J A R O X F R U
N I M R U D H E E R C X V A L
U V I H T A R T R B D N U M B
Z Y H A A I L L E N U A U L A
D D J S D M H I G B A S B E N
G E O U E E A W B D N U P R A
O A L T L D P T E A O I M A R
S S D P H J A R H I K S M A
H V I A H A A K K A N A H I H
V K K P R I N R O G I B E O N
V F V E P A S U M O S M O H P
M A S A D A B Y D O S S Q Z E
E N G E D I R W M A Z A G G F
```

◇ Bonus Trivia

Does the Bible state that Delilah cut Samson's hair?

No! (Judges 16:19)

93

46

Archaeological Sites of Bible Lands # 2

AI	SAMARIA
ALEPPO	SARDIS
ANTIOCH	SHAPUR
BOZRAH	SHILOH
BYBLOS	SUSA
CARMEL	TANIS
CORINTH	TARSUS
CUTHAH	THEBES
DERBE	THYATIRA
DIBON	TYRE
DJOKHA	UMMAH
NAZARETH	UR
NOB	WARKA
PALMYRA	YIRON
PERGA	ZINCIRLI
PHILIPPI	ZOAN
QUMRAN	

```
D H T H J H T N I R O C S W P
U I G H M Y B Y B L O S H B E
X R B L Y M N W G W I A A O R
A M M O F A A L Y L R O P N G
C I A M N R T A R Z I N U A A
A H S H K S L I O O A I R I T
R O U A E E C B R Z Y Y R A X
M L S B P N H T A A M A R I A
E I E P I A A R X L M S P N N
L H O Z H N E J A A U P O A T
T S E T I T O P S S I R R I I
U N U S H A M M U L I M G B O
G C J U N A O Z I Y U B N Z C
M A H K O J D H H Q T Y R E H
B E B R E D P S I D R A S B H
```

47

Archaeological Sites of Bible Lands # 3

EMMAUS	KEDESH
ENKOMI	KHARGA
ERIDU	LACHISH
ESHTEMOA	LARSA
GAMALA	MAMRE
GERASA	MEGIDDO
GIZA	MEMPHIS
HALUZA	MILETUS
HASANLU	MIZPAH
HATTUSHA	NIPPUR
IMWAS	NUZI
ISIN	OLYMPIA
JERASH	OPIS
JERICHO	PELLA
JOPPA	PETRA
KANISH	PYLOS

```
G E N K O M I S I P O C E B M
A B A S S U T E L I M R K E A
M G P Z A L D N I S I E M Z J
A K O E U N I Z F D D P I D O
L A H A T L I E U E H G C C P
A I C O S R A S S I C G W L P
S P I L E A A H S F P E L L A
U M R A R C R T O D D I G E M
A Y E C M L U E U H S I N A K
M L J H A A P M G H S A W M I
M O I I M R P O M I Z P A H U
E D Z S V S I A J E R A S H V
A S U H Q A N G X C S O L Y P
A S N G H A S A N L U E A A A
K H A R G A H A T T U S H A V
```

◇ **Bonus Trivia**

Where did Elijah find Elisha?

In a field plowing (1 Kings 19:19)

48

Archaeological Sites
of Bible Lands # 4

ARBELA

AROER

ATHENS

AZOR

AZU

BABYLON

BELVIOR

BETHLEHEM

GILGAL

GORAZIN

GORDION

HESHBON

HIPPOS

IZMIR

JEMDET

KISIGA

KNOSSUS

KURNUB

KURSI

MALATYA

MARLIK

MEDEBA

MERSIN

SINOPE

SMYRNA

SPARTA

TELLOH

TIBERIAS

TIRZAH

```
L S H N O L Y B A B T I G H J
A Q O F T H V X V M E S I A U
R Z E P O N I S K A D R L Z Z
M J O L P M L U I L M U G R A
D E L R A I R S S A E K A I J
W E H R R N H M I T J E L T I
T B L E U A P Y G Y R K G J Z
U I O B L T E R A A A N O N M
K R T L K H A N M I T O R O I
A M B P H E T A B A R S A I R
L E I I Q N R E L E A S Z D O
E R L T Y S F L B V P U I R V
B S M E D E B A S J S S N O V
R I H L R T I B E R I A S G S
A N O B H S E H B E L V I O R
```

Bonus Trivia

What verse in the Bible reveals that the earth is round?

Isaiah 40:22

49

Jesus is (the). . .

ALPHA

COMING

COUNSELOR

CREATOR

DIVINE

DOOR

ETERNAL

EVERLASTING

FATHER

GOD

HOLY

I AM

IN US

LAMB

LIFE

LOVE

MIGHTY

OMEGA

PEACE

PERFECT

PRINCE

PROPITIATION

REDEEMER

RISEN

SALVATION

SINLESS

TRUTH

WAY

WONDERFUL

WORD

WORKING

WORSHIPPED

```
L A M B G N I K R O W O R D C
L P C K N O I T A V L A S R L
R O G G Y W O R S H I P P E D
O N V N L U F R E D N O W H Y
O S O E I R O T A E R C T T W
D M I I E T G H H A L P H A X
C W E N T C S O T E B G R F E
C O A G L A A A D U I Q E E X
M O U Y A E I E L M R T D T I
Y J M N N J S T P R C T E E A
L G B I S J N S I E E C E R M
O F V T N E H I F P N V M N L
H I A Q S G L R N I O G E A I
D G N I M J E O R U X R R L F
G L R J F P Z P R M S X P C E
```

◇ Bonus Trivia

Where in the Bible is it revealed that this planet is suspended in space?

Job 26:7

50

Hebrew Months, Feasts, Sabbaths, & Other Holidays

AB	NISAN
ABIB	PENTECOST
ADAR	PURIM
ATONEMENT	SABBATH
BOOTHS	SEBAT
BUL	SECOND
CHISLEU	SIVAN
DEDICATION	SUCCOTH
ELUL	TABERNACLES
ETHANIM	TAMMUZ
FIRST	TEBETH
HARVEST	TISRI
INGATHERING	TRUMPETS
LIGHTS	WAVE
LOTS	WEEKS
NEW YEAR	ZIPH

```
N Q J H F P E N T E C O S T P
N I D Y T A B E R N A C L E S
L O S D N O C E S E B A T U I
O B I A S A C T S E V R A H N
T I X T N A G C V K U Q T M G
S B M O A H B A U M X S T I A
Q A K N Q C W B P S R R I N T
T E B E T H I E A I A A S A H
Q L C M C S T D F T D E R H E
N I H E A S H E E W H Y I T R
A G I N B D L T G D R W Z E I
V H S T Z U A A O S K E E W N
I T L O L J L R N O X N B K G
S S E T A M M U Z M B A T K R
S M U M I R U P Z I P H J M H
```

Bonus Trivia

Who moved the stone at Jesus' tomb and then sat on it?

An angel (Matthew 28:2)

51

Wives in the Bible

ABIAH

ABIGAIL

ACHSAH

ADAH

AHINOAM

ASENATH

BAARA

BILHAH

DEBORAH

EGLAH

EVE

HAGAR

HANNAH

HODESH

HODIAH

HUSHIM

JAEL

JEZEBEL

JOANNA

JUDITH

KETURAH

LEAH

MARY

MERAB

MICHAL

MILCAH

NAOMI

ORPAH

PENINNAH

RACHEL

RUTH

SARAH

SARAI

TAMAR

ZILPAH

```
L J B L P I A R A S O X S P H
E E A M A O N I H A H E B A H
A Z A Z J H K O C J V T S U H
H E R I L H U V R E O H U A A
J B A L H H A S P P C A I R R
S E G P A L A I H A A B N O A
N L H A N H A N D I A H H N S
A C O H N A A H N O M A T Z A
O B D A I R B S C A H L I L M
M W E R N O A R E I H G D L I
I T S U E B R C A N M E U E L
M H H T P E E E H G A Y J A C
T A N E F D M G T E A T R J A
J D Z K V R A M A T L H H A H
H A H L I B L L I A G I B A M
```

⬦ **Bonus Trivia**

Who chose soldiers by the way they drank water?

God (for Gideon) (Judges 7:4–5)

52

Buried

AARON	JEPHTHAH
ABDON	JOAB
ABINADAB	JONATHAN
ABNER	JOSHUA
ABRAHAM	LEAH
AHITHOPHEL	MIRIAM
BARZILLAI	MOSES
DAVID	RACHEL
EGYPTIANS	REBEKAH
ELON	RUTH
GIDEON	SAMSON
IBZAN	SAMUEL
ISAAC	SARAH
JACOB	SAUL
JAIR	TOLA

```
M J A C O B T M S H M I E H L
N O E D I G C A A W A S G A E
I T O L A Q E I M G H A Y H H
A A M O S E S R S J A A P T P
U M L T L S C I O O R C T H O
H A F L A O E M N S B I I P H
S S B M I S S B R H A G A E T
I N U D R Z A A Y U N N N J I
K E W A O O R D R A A S S Y H
L R M V R N A A E Z H A U H A
A A H I P E H N B B T A L L Q
M C S D R A N I E G A R I E N
I H A U C U H B K G N O Q A O
L E U H S A T A A N O N J H L
P L L B U F C H H Z J A N O E
```

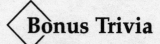

Bonus Trivia

Who was released from prison by an angel?

Peter (Acts 12:6–9)

53

Beautiful

ABIGAIL	GREY HEAD
ABSALOM	HOLINESS
BATHSHEBA	HOUSE
BRANCH	JERUSALEM
CAPTIVE	KING
COUNTENANCE	LORD
CROWN	MOUNT ZION
DIADEM	OLIVE TREE
ESTHER	ORNAMENT
EVERYTHING	PERFECTION
FEET	RACHEL
FLOCK	ROD
GARMENTS	SHULAMITE
GATE	ZION
GEMS	

```
B S H U L A M I T E D O R W G
N O I Z D I A D E M F X D K G
M O L A S B A P R E H T S E B
G D A E H Y E R G B N E T A G
E G G A R M E N T S Y A A Z Q
M D R O L P E R F E C T I O N
S K S S E N I L O H E L X K C
N I G N I H T Y R E V E X C A
L N N E B A T H S H E B A O P
I G W S O L I V E T R E E L T
A M O U N T Z I O N B O G F I
G Y R O J E R U S A L E M E V
I N C H L E H C A R W S R E E
B E E C N A N E T N U O C T G
A O R N A M E N T H C N A R B
```

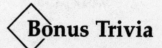 **Bonus Trivia**

Who commanded: "Search the scriptures"?

Christ (John 5:39)

109

54

Secrets

ALMS	LORD
BREAD	LOVE
CHAMBERS	MEN
COUNSEL	NAME
DREAM	PARTS
ENTICED	PLACE
ERRAND	PRESENCE
FACES	SEARCH
FAULTS	SHOOT
FEAR	SINS
FLEE	SPOKEN
GIFT	SPY
GOD	TABERNACLE
HEART	THINGS
JOB	WISDOM

```
G O D M S T A B E R N A C L E
W I S D O M S D E C I T N E P
W R P A R T S P M S N S W L D
R A E F M O E A O H F A C E S
J H Z W S V E T C K Y D M Z L
F S Y H O R V R F C E B C E E
V L O L D S A M B I Z N N A S
S O E H E E R O W H G U M E N
T T Z E S Y J E D A E R B S U
X Q L L D T Y F B D Z A M T O
J J O U H P P N O M N L R G C
A R S I A O S E N N A A S T N
D J N Z C F J M P W J H R B O
D G I Q P R E S E N C E C R W
S Z S Z U G E C A L P O D G E
```

◇ Bonus Trivia

Who advised her husband to steal a
vineyard?

Jezebel (1 Kings 21:15)

111

55

Seed in the Bible

AARON	JACOB
ABEL	JAPHETH
ABRAM	KINGS
ADULTERER	LOT
BARLEY	MAN
BEAST	MINGLED
BLESSED	MUSTARD
CAST	NOAH
CORIANDER	ROTTEN
DAVID	ROYAL
EPHRAIM	SAUL
EVE	SERPENT
FIELD	SETH
GODLY	SHEM
GRASS	SOWING
HAM	SPOILED
HERB	TREE
HOLY	WICKED
ISAAC	ZADOK
ISRAEL	

```
B A R L E Y C O R I A N D E R
U H O L Y Z Q S P O I L E D Q
W M E H S A D U L T E R E R J
I D Y D B S O W I N G S S A D
C H R R L T N E P R E S P G E
K K E A N E J X T T N H O G L
E H O I T A I F H E E D R E G
D I Y D C S M F T T L A B T N
K R S O A I U T H Y S A X D I
N O B R T Z O M S S F G J V M
O Y D T A R M I S A A C N M M
A A O A S E E A R U E B A I B
H L U B V A L E H L K B R C K
N O R A A I C W V E V E U A H
B L E S S E D E P H R A I M M
```

◇ Bonus Trivia

Concerning what man did Paul say "that he did me much evil"?

Alexander, the coppersmith (2 Timothy 4:14)

113

56

Second Things

BEAST	PIGEON
BOWL	PILLAR
BRETHREN	PRIEST
BULLOCK	RANK
CHARIOT	RIVER
CHILD	ROW
COMMANDMENT	SABBATH
COVENANT	SACRIFICE
CURTAIN	SEAL
DAY	SON
DEATH	SORT
DEGREE	TIME
HOUSE	TRUMPET
LETTER	TURTLEDOVE
LOT	VEIL
MAN	WARD
MIRACLE	WOE
MONTH	YEAR
ORDER	

```
O R N W C E R E S Y D E R L P
X A A H T I T C R A E A I I I
M R I L V N E R U E B A Y E G
D L T E L W E C U R T B R V E
D O R R O I F M I M T T A E O
D T S R O L P B D F P A E T N
E H Y S W S T R K N I E I L H
A C T O Q F S E K C A R T N D
T H B N M V E T N B O M C P O
H A E U O V I H A S E L M A O
I R S O K M R R R G Z A L O S
T I U R E G P E W L A E S U C
E O O D T N A N E V O C J T B
O T H E X E V O D E L T R U T
W E E R G E D G E L C A R I M
```

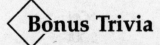

◇ Bonus Trivia

Who saw a vision of a valley of dry bones?

Ezekiel (37:1–14)

57

Waited
(for, at, in, & on)

ALTAR	LIGHT
BEAR	LORD
BLOOD	MAN
BUSINESS	MINISTERING
CONTINUALLY	NAME
CORNER	OFFICE
DECEIVE	PAUL
ELIHU	PRIESTS
FIELD	PREY
GATE	PROMISE
GIBEAH	RAIN
GOD	ROBBERS
GOOD	SALVATION
HOPE	SON
ISLES	SOUL
JEWS	SWORD
JOB	THEE
KING	VINEYARDS
LEVITES	WICKED

```
L O F F I C E K C O R N E R S
T H E E S T S E I R P V G A O
H A E B I G J V H O P E A T N
Y L L A U N I T N O C B T L L
L U O S H I W H U H I L E A E
R O B B E R S D E K C I W Q V
U S P L J E V P R O M I S E I
D A R O E T I H F I E L D Q T
E L E R W S N G S W O R D D E
C V Y D S I E B U S I N E S S
E A N O B N Y I D B O J R K L
I T A G L I A S O M E A L I I
V I M K O M R L O A I G U N G
E O E C O L D E G N G T A G H
F N T D D K S S R A E B P Q T
```

◇ **Bonus Trivia**

How long did Job live after his trouble?

140 years (Job 42:16)

117

58

Awake in the Bible

AIM	JESUS
DAVID	JOHN
DEBORAH	LAZARUS
DEED	LORD
DRUNKARDS	MAN
EAR	MIGHTY
GLORY	PETER
GOD	PSALTERY
HARP	SAMSON
HEART	SHULAMITE
HEATHEN	SWORD
JACOB	WATCHMAN
JAMES	WIND
JEREMIAH	WOOD
JERUSALEM	ZION

```
C L P S A L T E R Y K N J E R
K B O C N Y N D T B S D T T E
E E A R X X A E F B D L H I T
H R J O W W M E X Q R D A M E
E S A Q A Y A D Z E A E I A P
T L C Y H G I M P K B M L M
S N O U C P O W U R N O E U E
U H B I H N H O O A U R R H L
R O C B M G E O S H R A E S A
A J A D A O A D F D H J W S
Z J Y I N D T H M S Z D B I U
A B A R M V H E S U G R D N R
L F X M O V E A O S W O R D E
X G L B E L N R N Z D L O X J
V J E S U S G T D I V A D M R
```

Bonus Trivia

What Old Testament book does Jesus quote more than any other?

Deuteronomy

119

59
Fear (of, in, & not)

ABIMELECH	JUDAH
ABRAM	KING
ALMIGHTY	LAND
ARMY	LEVI
ASHER	LORD
BAASHA	LOVE
BRIERS	MAN
DAN	MARY
DEATH	MOSES
EARTH	NIGHT
EVIL	PAUL
FLESH	REPROACH
FLOCK	REUBEN
GAD	SEED
GOD	SIMEON
ISAAC	SIMON
ISRAEL	SWORD
ISSACHAR	TORMENT
JACOB	ZACHARIAS
JEWS	ZEBULUN

```
Y Z E B U L U N M A R B A I D
R A I D A Y R A M L L O R D S
E X L S H A B P R E U B E N L
H H J M S C S S O A H A D U J
S X C E I A A H E R D E A T H
A M N E W G C O A S L P Z E J
J A D O L S H H R I O L A N D
G N I K E E L T A P V M C S T
B O C A J M M I Y R E T H W H
I V E L G H I I V Y P R A O G
S J H G S A V S B E B E R R I
A V C E L B D O G A A A I D N
A F L O C K D A N R R P A E E
C F S R E I R B T M E V S E M
T O R M E N T H Y N O M I S R
```

Bonus Trivia

Who wanted to buy the power of the Holy Spirit?

Simon the sorcerer (Acts 8:18–19)

60
King David's Allies & Friends

ABIATHAR	JONATHAN
ABISHAI	JORAM
ACHISH	MACHIR
ADORAM	MEPHIBOSHETH
AHIMAAZ	NAHASH
BARZILLAI	NATHAN
BENAIAH	REI
GAD	SAMUEL
HAMATH	SHEVA
HIRAM	SHOBI
HUSHAI	TOI
IRA	TYRE
ITTAI	URIAH
JEHOSHAPHAT	ZADOK
JOAB	

```
M K I M H A M T I O T Z K A M
A N K Z J O A B M A R I H O A
R A B I S H A I A J O R A M C
O S H O B I F H T A M A H T H
D O J E H O S H A P H A T J I
A I P Q H A I A N E B S O R R
H S A H A N Z C Q N H N T A U
N I M L W P I E R E A W C H Q
Z T H C L U N U V T B H V T G
A T E U R I S A H L S Z F A K
A A E I S I Z A T I E P D I O
M I A R R H N R H H Z U S B D
I H S A Y N A C A M A P M A A
H K U H T T A I U B V N P A Z
A N M E P H I B O S H E T H S
```

◇ **Bonus Trivia**

What prophet was commanded to lie for 390 days upon his left side, and 40 days upon his right?

Ezekiel (Ezekiel 4:4–6)

61
King David's Family

ABIGAIL

ABINADAB

ABISHAG

ABITAL

ABSALOM

ADONIJAH

AHINOAM

AMNON

BATHSHEBA

BOAZ

EGLAH

ELIAB

ELIADA

ELIPHELET

ELISHAMA

ELISHUA

HAGGITH

IBHAR

ITHREAM

JAPHIA

JESSE

MAACAH

MICHAL

NAHASH

NATHAN

NEPHEG

OBED

RUTH

SHOBAB

SOLOMON

ZERUIAH

```
I Y T E L E H P I L E S S E J
B A E L I K M Y N E L I A D A
I I T H R E A M W H T U R H L
N E P H E G O M I C H A L T I
A A M N O N N D H S A B X I A
T B I Z E P I E A O B E T G G
H A U U L F H B L L I H I G I
A D M M I A A O G O T S B A B
N A H A S A I D E M A H H H A
R N A B H B N H O O L T A S E
M I I A U S Q A P N J A R I L
Z B U B A A I K H A I B H B I
A A R O K L Y L A A J J B A A
O S E H O O N P E O S K A A B
B R Z S X M M A A C A H W H V
```

◇ Bonus Trivia

On what island was John when he wrote the Revelation?

Patmos (Revelation 1:9)

125

62
New Testament Men

ARISTOBULUS

CARPUS

CYRENIUS

DEMAS

DEMETRIUS

DIOTREPHES

ERASTUS

EUBULUS

GAIUS

HERMES

HERODION

JASON

LINUS

LUCAS

NARCISSUS

NEREUS

OLYMPAS

ONESIPHORUS

PATROBAS

PHILOLOGUS

PUDENS

RUFUS

SILVANUS

SOSIPATER

SOSTHENES

TERTIUS

TITUS

URBANE

ZENAS

```
S U I R T E M E D S U E R E N
O U R B A N E P U D E N S R R
N X Y N S E N E H T S O S A E
E N L A C E S S T U P U A S T
S O S R C S H A U E I T C T A
I S U C D H U P N N R H U U P
P A L I I E P E E A T L S I I
H J U S S G M R R R Z V I H S
O S B S U I Y A M A T Z L U O
R A O U L C T T S E C O T I S
U P T S U Z L I N U S S I T S
S M S U B H E R O D I O N D U
Z Y I F U S A B O R T A P R I
G L R U E S U G O L O L I H P
T O A R S U I A G T I T U S G
```

◇ Bonus Trivia

What verse of Scripture reveals the great secret of physical life?

The life of the flesh is in the blood.
(Leviticus 17:11)

63
King David's Enemies

ABSALOM	MAACAH
AHITHOPHEL	MOAB
AMALEKITES	NABAL
AMMON	PHILISTINES
BETAH	REHOB
DOEG	SAPH
EDOM	SAUL
GESHURITES	SHEBA
GEZRITES	SHIMEI
GOLIATH	SHOBACH
HADADEZER	SIPPAI
HADAREZER	SYRIA
HANUN	TOB
ISHBIBENOB	ZOBAH
LAHMI	

```
T C L B E T A H Y F S J F N F
H H H C A B O H S E T T P Q S
A U A G E Z R I T E S N D N E
N Z B F F O G I A E A M G B T
U A E I D O R B F B R O H O I
N Q H U L U S F A E R A A N K
I B S I H A P L Z O E B D E E
X O A S L H M E G K H G A B L
Z T E O A B D A M M O N R I A
H G M B I A P P I S B A E B M
O B O E D O M A A C A H Z H A
H Z R A W A T S A U L H E S H
P S H I M E I M H A L J R I O
A H I T H O P H E L S Y R I A
S E N I T S I L I H P G E O D
```

Bonus Trivia

Who had only a weapon of water which was used to defeat the Egyptians?

Moses (Exodus 14:21–28)

64

Places Where David & His Men Roamed

ADULLAM	JATTIR
APHEK	JEBUS
AROER	JEZREEL
ATHACH	MAHANAIM
BESOR	MAON
BETHEL	MIZPAH
CARMEL	MOAB
CHORASHAN	NAIOTH
ENGEDI	NOB
ESHTEMOA	PARAN
GATH	RACHAL
GILGAL	RAMAH
HACHILAH	RAMOTH
HARETH	ZIKLAG
HEBRON	ZIPH
HORMAH	

```
K E G W U H A C H I L A H N N
H N I R O S E B M A L L U D A
A G L L L M E B Q H Q Z O Z I
R E G N E E I L R J A H I M O
E D A N A M E Z A O E B T P T
T I L G L H R R P A N B A A H
H J B A O M S A Z A Q P U R G
O B S O B M Z A C E H I A S A
R O J M E V I O R E J C A H H
E N A E T H K A K O H H R H C
S Z T T H A L M N A H T O A A
H F T H E M A Q L A R C E M H
D P I S L R G O O A H I R A T
H N R E Q O D M A O N A K R A
N A R A P H T O M A R N M P V
```

◇ Bonus Trivia

What man ate a little book in his mouth that was sweet, but afterward it became bitter?

John (Revelation 10:10)

65

More New Testament Men

ANNAS	LEVI
APOLLOS	LUKE
BARTHOLOMEW	MALCHUS
BARTIMAEUS	MARCUS
CORNELIUS	MARK
ELIAS	MATTHEW
EPAENETUS	MOSES
HEROD	PAUL
JAIRUS	PETER
JAMES	PILATE
JESUS	STEPHANAS
JOHN	THOMAS
JOSEPH	TYCHICUS
JUDAS	ZACHARIAS
JUDE	ZELOTES
JUSTUS	

```
O S A V S E M A J J A I R U S
T A O V W L H B J E S U S E U
S A I L E E U P E T E R T P I
S U H C L A M K E M V O G A L
J E Z K N O E O E S L Q U E E
S O S N Q T P M L E O J M N N
A U A O A F H A Z O T J A E R
I S C L M M E T D J H L R T O
R E I I X A R T E U O T K U C
A P U F H R O H D S M W R S C
H L E V I C D E U T A R C A J
C A L Z E U Y W J U S D M O B
A J U D A S U T S S I N H B P
Z B A R T I M A E U S N H Z T
V E P D X S A N A H P E T S I
```

◇ Bonus Trivia

Name two kings who could not interpret their own dreams.

Pharaoh and Nebuchadnezzar

66
New Testament Women

ANNA	MARTHA
APPHIA	MARY
CANDACE	PERSIS
DAMARIS	PHEBE
DAMSEL	PRISCILLA
DORCAS	RHODA
DRUSILLA	SALOME
ELISABETH	SAMARITAN
EUNICE	SAPPHIRA
EUODIAS	SUSANNA
HERODIAS	SYNTYCHE
JOANNA	TABITHA
JULIA	TRYPHENA
LOIS	TRYPHOSA
LYDIA	VIRGINS
MAGDALENE	

```
E H L S R E E B E H P T S L C
U P I N J M A T A B I T H A A
N A F I O O A H T R A M O S N
I L D G A L J U L I A N I N D
C L A R N A A K G M A O D S A
E I M I N S A R A T L Q Y S C
U S A V A N A G I T Q N O D E
O U R Y N S D R R H T H O A L
D R I A I A A Y E Y P R P M I
I D S S L M P R C Y C P A V S
A U R E A H O H R A H R A N A
S E N S E D E T S I Y O P S B
P E L N I A N N A A D O H R E
D K A A E A L L I C S I R P T
I D S L Y D I A L E S M A D H
```

Bonus Trivia

Who was the father of John the Baptist?

Zacharias (Luke 1:59-63)

135

67

King David's Victories

ABEL	JEBUS
AMMAH	JERUSALEM
AMMON	KEILAH
BEAR	LION
BEROTHAI	METHEG
BETAH	MOAB
BETHLEHEM	PERAZIM
DAMASCUS	RABBAH
ELAH	REPHAIM
EPHRAIM	SHAARAIM
EUPHRATES	SYRIA
GATH	TELAIM
GEZER	VALLEY OF SALT
GOB	ZION
GOLIATH	ZOBAH
HELAM	

```
E U P H R A T E S X F S B O G
M Z V A H Z U A B M L I O N T
I R E O O N M E J O H D D U L
Z B C B O I R M I A L E T J A
A M A M A O R H L G G B H E S
R H M H T A E I J O E M A B F
E A P H B M E E L T I Z T U O
P E A B E K R I H A M S E S Y
R I A T N U A L R A U O B R E
F H H F S T E A M C M U A P L
L E B A H H A A S W R M H B L
G U L N E H L A J G H R A J A
S E O M S E M N A A A H H U V
M I N W H A D T L I Y N Z U Q
Z J G K D K H E M F A I R Y S
```

Bonus Trivia

By the use of what word does the Bible describe an atheist?

The fool (Psalm 14:1)

68

Treacherous

ABIMELECH	JEHOZABAD
ABSALOM	JEHU
AHAB	JEZEBEL
AHITHOPHEL	JOAB
AMNON	JONADAB
ATHALIAH	JOZACHAR
BAANAH	JUDAS
BAASHA	LEVI
BALAAM	MENAHEM
CAIN	PEKAH
DAVID	RECHAB
DOEG	SHALLUM
GIBEAH	SIMEON
HAMAN	ZIBA
HOSHEA	ZIMRI

```
L E B E Z E J J C A L G C B O
B M B A D A N O J B W E A A D
S I O R B O R F X I N O C H U
N I J L D A V I D Z E D A C S
A O M U A S A H A B D M I E H
A B N E D S V S S V A B N R A
G H I M O A B Z H N B L H E L
I W I M A N S A V A A E A A L
B C R T E G I Z U K Z M I E U
E W Z R H L P V H H O A L H M
A B C M O O E I E E H A A S Z
H H A K E P P C J L E L H O I
C N B A A N A H H G J A T H M
J O Z A C H A R E C O B A U R
H X M E N A H E M L B A O J I
```

◇ Bonus Trivia

Who was sent by God to restore Saul's
eyesight?

Ananias (Acts 9:10-12)

69

Towns Joshua Conquered

ACHSHAPH	JARMUTH
ADULLAM	JERICHO
AI	JERUSALEM
APHEK	JOKNEAM
ARAD	KEDESH
BETHEL	LACHISH
DEBIR	LIBNAH
DOR	MADON
EGLON	MAKKEDAH
GEDER	MEGIDDO
GEZER	MEROM
GILGAL	SHIMRON
HAZOR	TAANACH
HEBRON	TAPPUAH
HEPHER	TIRZAH
HORMAH	

```
H H A D E K K A M J R Q H I R
A O H C I R E J F E E T A E R
M Q Q M A D O N M D U T D L H
R D D A R A R G O M E E A N S
O C H A H O N R R U G G B A E
H B S W Z X J A E F L L T A D
O E I A P F J K M I R O A N E
O T H I Q B V E G Q E N A O K
D H C M A L L U D A Z O N R N
D E A T T A H R I B E D A B O
I L L C S G Y E A K G R C E R
G H A U P P A T P E E V H H M
E P R D U A C H S H A P H D I
M E M A E N K O J P E I I N H
J H A N B I L O H A Z R I T S
```

◇ **Bonus Trivia**

Is the forbidden fruit identified as an apple
in the Bible?

No

70
Drunk in the Bible

AMMON	HARLOT
ARABIA	ISRAEL
ASHDOD	JERUSALEM
ASHKELON	JUDAH
BABYLON	MEDES
BELSHAZZAR	MOAB
BENHADAD	NABAL
BUZ	NOAH
CORINTHIANS	PHAROAH
DEDAN	SHESHACH
EDOM	SIDON
EGYPT	TEMA
EKRON	TYRE
ELAH	URIAH
ELAM	UZ
EPHRAIM	ZIMRI
GAZA	

```
O R M B R B E N H A D A D E A
M A A T H A O R A H P Y I S K
E Z L M A T Z J U S E A H W F
L Z E Z I E W Z H L S K G B Y
A A N I B M U E A H E A U E X
S H A M A A S H D L Z Z H D F
U S B R R H A O O A S I D O N
R L A I A M D N M B A O M M R
E E L C M B T Y H A R L O T T
J B H O B A B Y L O N O R K E
A S N A I H T N I R O C H Q A
M E D E S I H A F L E A R S I
F N A D E D A N P B T P Y G E
T Y R E V F O N H A D U J T E
H A I R U F N D E P H R A I M
```

Bonus Trivia

How many books of the Bible did James write?

One

71

Colors in the Bible

AMETHYST	GREEN
BDELLIUM	HAZEL
BLACK	IRON
BLUE	JASPER
BRASS	ONYX
BRONZE	PEARL
BROWN	PURPLE
CHESTNUT	RED
CLEAR	SAPPHIRE
COPPER	SARDIUS
CRIMSON	SCARLET
EMERALD	SILVER
GOLD	TOPAZ
GOLDEN	WHITE
GRAY	WOOL

```
P U R P L E L U L T V S L G R
L F J M T V X B O X Y N O B E
F O V N S S Z P G E D L R Z P
Z W O M C C A S W P D R J C S
Z R G W V Z A X I E T I H W A
I T C O P P E R N E E R G D J
Y G D B E U L B L A C K D Q O
J R L S F H N W B E L E Z A H
E A A C H E S T N U T G V O L
Z Y R H L Y D C R I M S O N F
N P E A R L B D E L L I U M M
O H M A O D O E R I H P P A S
R A E G X M E S A R D I U S A
B L S D N W O R B R A S S Q R
C S I L V E R T S Y H T E M A
```

◇ **Bonus Trivia**

Who suffered many things in a dream
because of Jesus?

Pilate's wife (Matthew 27:19)

145

72

Brothers in the Bible

AARON	KOHATH
ARELI	MERARI
ARODI	MOSES
ELON	OHAD
ER	ONAN
ERI	PEREZ
EZBON	PHUVAH
GERSHON	SERED
HAGGI	SHELAH
HAMUL	SHIMRON
HEZRON	SHUAL
JACHIN	SHUNI
JAHLEEL	TOLA
JAMIN	ZERAH
JEMUEL	ZIPHION
JOB	ZOHAR

```
N X Y H T A H O K Z E R E P S
O R Z Z U M G S H E Z R O N H
A N L E E L E W C R R N L K U
R V O R R S R A T I A U A M A
E M A L O A S V D N M S Z B L
L R U M E D H U O A J E U T L
I S H I M R O N H W Y R J O B
X I L C W J N B R E S E B Z O
G E G E I N U H S D H D I N C
L Z J G E F N G I A D P L I Z
E B A J A L J O V D H N Z H O
U O M T S H H U R I O C Z C H
M N I O M O H A O A G R G A A
E D N L K P A N J I A J A J R
J N D A H O S H E L A H S R K
```

Bonus Trivia

What man for his own protection in a foreign country pretended that he was insane?

David (1 Samuel 21:10-15)

73

More Brothers in the Bible

ANDREW	ISHUI
ARD	JAHZEEL
ASHBEL	JAMES
BECHER	JEHOAHAZ
BELA	JEHOIACHIN
BERIAH	JESUS
EHI	JEZER
ELIAKIM	JOHN
GERA	JUDE
GUNI	MALCHIEL
HEBER	MUPPIM
HUPPIM	NAAMAN
HUSHIM	PETER
IMNAH	ROSH
ISHUAH	SHILLEM

```
L N A M A A N C H U S H I M R
A O U M C R E M I P P U M F E
A S W C I S E N S R G I H E H
H N H M H P E B H J J G V I C
D A D I I A P N E E A M G S E
F R U R L J N U J H H I R H B
O H A H E L S M H O Z K B U A
S S A Z S W E G I I E A E I S
U O E V N I U M I A E I R U H
S R W H S N W A L C L L I V B
E F O E I S J E M H P E A G E
J J M X L T B K V I E Y H B L
Z A H A O H E J Y N T E D U J
J U L E I H C L A M E X O B A
N Z W Z A R E G L L R C T O Y
```

◇ Bonus Trivia

Is this in the Bible? "If anyone does not love the Lord Jesus Christ, let him be accursed."

74

Towers in the Bible

BABEL
CASTLE
CORNER
DAVID
DESERT
DESOLATE
EDAR
FLOCK
FURNACES
GREAT
HANANEEL
HIGH
IVORY
JEZREEL
JOTHAM

LEBANON
MEAH
PENUEL
PROJECTING
SALVATION
SHECHEM
SILOAM
STRONG
SYENE
TYRE
TYRUS
UZZIAH
WATCH
WATCHMEN

```
W G D A V I D G K C O L F H P
A J N S N O N A B E L L G H E
T M O I H A E M M A H I T A N
C I Y T T E Z E R E H S R N U
H V D S H C C A X D B T E A E
M O W E A A E H U A A R S N L
E R L Z S L M J E R B O E E J
N Y C I C O V C O M E N D E B
A U A V W T L A U R L G Z L U
F C S A V Y F A T H P R O M Z
Z U T A E R G D T I E T Y A Z
G C L N K U S M P E O R P O I
H W E S N S B Z L M R N Z L A
K Y Z S E C A N R U F S B I H
S N L C O R N E R T Y R E S W
```

◇ Bonus Trivia

Who did David say the Lord would laugh at?

The wicked (Psalm 37:12–13)

75

Walls in the Bible

ASHDOD

BABYLON

BETHSHAN

BOWING

BRASEN

COURT

DAMASCUS

EAST

FALLEN

FENCED

FIRE

GATH

GAZA

GREAT

HIGH

IRON

JABNEH

JASPER

JERICHO

JERUSALEM

JEZREEL

JUDAH

MIDDLE

OPHEL

PALACE

RABBAH

SHELAH

TEMPLE

TYRUS

WHITED

ZION

```
E C A L A P E N O L Y B A B M
N O R I A G N I W O B G D B S
V C J W J E Z R E E L O F E U
N S U C S A M A D H O H R T R
C E T F A L L E N G M C H H Y
J O S I C E L D D I M I A S T
J A U A C W K H E H R R B H D
O A S R R G A Z A T H E B A O
H D B P T B E K A L A J A N D
H E D N E P L L F E D E R U H
A T E R E R T E P B U F R P S
L I D Z Z H N S H M J D I G A
E H C I M C H N A P E V V R U
H W O F E G A T H E O T U F E
S N W D V J E R U S A L E M F
```

◇ Bonus Trivia

What book of the Bible records these words:
"whosoever will may come"?

None

76

Gates & Walls in Jerusalem

ASHER

BEAUTIFUL

BENJAMIN

BROAD

CORNER

DAN

DUNG

EAST

EPHRAIM

FIRST

FISH

FOUNTAIN

GAD

HORSE

INNER

JERUSALEM

JOSEPH

JUDAH

KINGS

LEVI

MIPHKAD

NAPHTALI

NEW

NORTH

OLD

PRISON

PROJECTING

REUBEN

SHEEP

SIMEON

SOUTH

VALLEY

ZEBULUN

```
D M B S O U T H F J O S E P H
U F E E P P R O J E C T I N G
N I K L N E T H H H A D U J S
G S O P A J E V T O U R M P G
G H L C Y S A H A R W E I M N
L K D I O L U M S S O N P I I
X U D P L R A R I E U N H A K
N A F E R N N N E N R I K R J
G U Y I E I A E R J E A A H P
U B L B T P S R R I H T D P D
L P U U H U F O J V S N N E A
H E T T B I A Q N E A U E Z N
R Q A S R E F E I L S O W J O
V L D S A L Z H B W Q F H H U
I O T N O E M I S D A O R B L
```

◇ **Bonus Trivia**

Name the book given to Jesus to read in the synagogue.

Isaiah (Luke 4:17)

77

Other Gates in the Bible

BATHRABBIM

BRASS

CAMP

CARBUNCLES

CHILDREN

COURT

DEATH

EKRON

FOUNDATION

GUARD

HEAVEN

HELL

HIGH

HIGHER

IRON

JOSHUA

KINGS

LEAVED

LORD

MIDDLE

PALACE

PEARL

PRAISE

SAMARIA

SHALLECHETH

SODOM

STRAIT

SUR

TENTS

TWELVE

ZION

```
P W E D M I B B A R H T A B E
C S U R E F I A U H S O J V K
H S N L O A O T L E A V E D R
I E E R H H T U W Q J D N P O
L L V A T Z I H N E O U O R N
D C A E E L H G D D L O I A G
R N E P H Z O I H C A V Z I U
E U H S C J E R G E A T E S A
N B W A E S S H D H R M I E R
Z R I M L G B T E Q S A P O D
L A M A L N R B R L M T J E N
N C B R A I A A T A L O N S P
H O U I H K S J R P I F D E P
P I R A S Z S C O U R T N O T
O I M I D D L E E C A L A P S
```

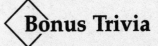

Bonus Trivia

Name the two men who feared a small child.

Pharaoh and Herod (Exodus 1:22 and Matthew 2:3)

78

Builders of the Wall

AZARIAH

BARUCH

BAVAI

BENJAMIN

BINNUI

EZER

GIBEON

HANUN

HASHABIAH

HASHUB

HATTUSH

JADON

JEDAIAH

JOIDA

LEVITES

MELATIAH

MIZPAH

NEHEMIAH

NETHINIM

PALAL

PEDAIAH

REHUM

REPHAIAH

SHALLUM

SHEMAIAH

UZZIEL

ZACCUR

ZADOK

ZEKOITES

```
H A I A D E J N L M M S H C J
I I A V A B O A A U K H A H A
S E T I V E L D L I O E P A D
H Q W P B A I L R A D M Z S O
A R A I P O A Q Z B A A I H N
T U G X J H F A U G Z I M A H
T C J A S I R H N U N A H B N
U C X U U I S B J S I H O I E
S A L N A A J R E P H A I A H
H Z N H H Z O H E N R N H H E
M I N I H T E N C R J S W D M
B V P E D A I A H U E A U A I
R H A I T A L E M I R H M X A
R E Z E L E I Z Z U B A U I H
E O N S E T I O K E Z B B M N
```

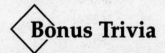

Bonus Trivia

Who buried Moses?

God (Deuteronomy 34:6)

79

Returning Exiles: Men Who Married Foreign Women

ABDI	JEREMAI
ADAIAH	MALLUCH
ADNA	MANASSEH
AMRAM	MATTATHAH
ATHLAI	MATTENAI
AZIZA	MESHULLAM
BANI	SHEAL
BEDEIAH	SHEMARIAH
BENAIAH	SHIMEI
BENJAMIN	SHIMEON
CHELAL	UEL
CHELLUH	VANIAH
ELIPHELET	ZABAD
JAASAU	ZABBAI
JASHUB	

```
F A F S H A I R A M E H S P B
Y J T A D A I A H M X R T O U
M T A H H C U L L A M H A H H
U O B Z A B A D U R Y A D T S
E E D M J T B V T M S H N E A
L M I A E S H A U A H T A L J
C Q A H I S H L N C I A S E M
H H M N E M H E A I M T H H L
E B E V A I A U A I E T I P B
L E R L A S A T L L O A M I J
L D E E A N S B T L N M E L A
U E J U U L I E B E A B I E A
H I A Z I Z A A H A N M P E S
Q A B E N A I A H H Z A W E A
C H B E N J A M I N L A I V U
```

◇ Bonus Trivia

What disciple forsook Paul for the love of the world?

Demas (2 Timothy 4:10)

80

Returning Exiles: Men Who Married Foreign Women #2

BENAIAH	JEREMOTH
BINNUI	JOEL
ELASAH	JOSEPH
ELEAZAR	JOZABAD
ELIASHIB	JUDAH
ELIJAH	MALCHIAH
ELIOENAI	MATTANIAH
HANANI	SHARAI
HANANIAH	SHASHAI
IDDO	SHIMEI
ISHMAEL	TELEM
JARIB	URI
JEHIEL	UZZIAH
JEHOHANAN	ZEBINA
JEIEL	ZECHARIAH

U	Z	Z	I	A	H	A	B	L	H	P	E	S	O	J
V	D	H	L	R	D	J	N	E	L	A	S	A	H	N
N	A	A	E	U	R	I	E	I	N	L	E	O	J	X
E	B	N	I	K	Q	E	S	H	B	A	Z	A	B	D
L	A	A	H	M	L	I	N	H	O	E	I	Y	P	P
I	Z	N	E	I	A	E	E	H	M	H	Z	A	X	H
O	O	I	J	R	T	L	A	H	R	A	A	H	H	B
E	J	A	A	H	I	I	T	A	S	I	E	N	V	I
N	H	H	A	A	R	O	Z	H	A	J	W	L	A	N
A	S	N	S	A	M	A	I	H	R	J	A	I	Y	N
I	E	H	H	E	E	M	S	T	E	U	B	R	U	U
L	I	C	R	L	E	A	E	I	A	D	N	U	I	I
B	E	E	E	I	H	L	E	I	N	A	N	A	H	B
Z	J	A	F	S	E	L	H	A	I	H	C	L	A	M
I	D	D	O	M	A	M	A	T	T	A	N	I	A	H

Bonus Trivia

What significance do these numbers have in connection with the study of the Bible: 66, 39, 27?

27 in the New Testament
39 in the Old Testament
66 books in the Bible

81

Returning Exiles: Leaders of Tribes & Family Heads

ADIN	JESHUA
ADONIKAM	LOD
ARAH	MISPERETH
ATER	MORDECAI
AZARIAH	NAHAMINI
AZGAD	NEHEMIAH
BEBAI	ONO
BEZAI	PAHATH
BIGVAI	PAROSH
BILSHAN	RAAMIAH
ELAM	SENAAH
HADID	SHEPHATIAH
HARIM	ZACCAI
HARIPH	ZATTU
HASHUM	ZERUBBABEL

```
O C M N H M O R D E C A I W S
N I I V T E H H H A R I M G H
O D U E S A H A A Z T I T H X
A A W R R H S P E I D J S W Z
N Z X A U H E R I O R O H E Y
A G A A U D U P L R R A B H H
H A T M W B H U H A A E Z A T
S D E I B T T I P A B H I A I
L N R A A T N S U A T M G A D
I B B H A I E H I I E I C J D
B E A Z M N S V E H A C A Y I
L P I A A E D L E L A V S H A
U Z H A J T F N C Z A D G J Z
N A H T E R E P S I M M I I E
N T U U A D O N I K A M I D B
```

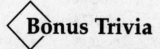

82

Family Heads of the Returning Nethinim

BAKBUK	MEHIDA
BARKOS	MEUNIM
BAZLITH	NEKODA
BESAI	NEPHISHESIM
GAHAR	NEZIAH
GAZZAM	PADON
GIDDEL	PASEAH
HAGABA	REAIAH
HAKUPHA	REZIN
HANAN	SHALMAI
HARHUR	SIA
HARSHA	SISERA
HASUPHA	TABBAOTH
HATIPHA	TAMAH
KEROS	UZZA
LEBANA	ZIHA

```
Z T F F P R L N C N J H H A W
A I U X A E V K A H A A H G S
D Q H H B H E N A R I P A I K
O E A A A R A E H Z U Z S U U
K G N I O H S U E S Z E S N B
E A A S P A R N A A R U A I K
N E L U P T N H M A V Y A Z A
R T K M J T A B B A O T H E B
U A D I H E M H B E S A I R A
H L E D D I G E A U H S F S Z
P W W N O D A P Q G C C C I L
T A M A H E S O K R A B T A I
M I S E H S I H P E N B T H T
G U M I N U E M A H S R A H H
S H A L M A I H A T I P H A L
```

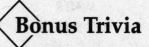

Bonus Trivia

Which came first: the chicken or the egg?

The chicken (Genesis 1:21–22)

83

Fountains in the Bible

ABOUNDING

BLESSED

BLOOD

BROKEN

CHAMBERS

CLEAVED

DEEP

DEVOURED

DISPERSED

DRIED

ELIM

FRESH

GARDENS

GATE

ISRAEL

JACOB

LIFE

NEPHTOAH

PIT

REPAIRED

SALT

SEALED

SHUR

STOPPED

STRENGTHENED

STRONG

TEARS

TROUBLED

TWELVE

VALLEYS

WATER

WILDERNESS

```
F S R A E T A S D E S S E L B
D D D D K G B D O O L B W D D
E E W E L S O G W M I L E Q E
V L S N E A U A A E F I L G L
O B Y E A L N T T N R S D H A
U U E H R T D E E D P E S A E
R O L T S S I U R I R S D O S
E R L G I H N H T I E I D T C
D T A N V U G D A N S C G H G
S E V E P R E P R P L A A P H
T V B R X E E E E E R M C E R
R L O T P R D A D B T K N F
O E C S X L S V E E F R E S H
N W A U I E E N R N E K O R B
G T J W D D S S D E P P O T S
```

Bonus Trivia

Is this in the Bible? "Cleanliness is next to godliness."

No (John Wesley said it)

169

84

Hope (. . .)

ABOUND	ISRAEL
ANCHOR	JESUS
BETTER	JEWS
BLESSED	JOY
CALLING	LAID UP
CHRIST	LORD
CONTINUALLY	PEOPLE
DOOR	PRISONERS
ETERNAL LIFE	REJOICE
FIRM	REST
GLORY	RESURRECTION
GOD	SECURE
GOOD	STEDFAST
GOSPEL	TO COME
GRACE	WORD

```
A S E R D L J B R P T S E R R
L R T E G R N O U B H J S Q O
P E E S G O O D Y F E S R J O
T N R U P P I W I W I E O V D
O O N R I A I R S S T C H F Y
C S A R L O M N R S L U C S L
O I L E J E Q A I E G R N T L
M R L C G N E R P I N E A E A
E P I T O L H S V F I G R D U
I A F I D C O P A B L L E F N
A H E O A G R E L E L O J A I
P T E N V G N O R T A R O S T
D N U O B A R P M T C Y I T N
J E S U S D K L K E H W C E O
B L E S S E D E G R A C E I C
```

◇ **Bonus Trivia**

Who was "without a blemish" in the Old Testament?

Absalom (2 Samuel 14:25)

85
Foundation in the Bible

ABIRAM

APOSTLES

BERYL

CHRYSOLYTE

CHRYSOPRASUS

CITY

CORNER

DUST

EARTH

EMERALD

GOD

GOLD

GOOD

HEAPS

HILLS

HOUSE

JACINTH

JASPER

JESUS

KIRHARESETH

MOUNTAINS

PRECIOUS

ROCK

SAPPHIRE

SARDIUS

SARDONYX

STONE

SURE

TOPAZ

WORLD

ZION

```
E H E M E R A L D H S R S H F
M T R E P S A J I U E Y A Z B
A A Y F V V B L S N T S R S E
R K J L Y N L E R I U S D N V
I A K S O S J O C S U L O Z L
B X P I A S C S A I R T N V H
A G D A R P Y R D O S N Y M T
N N O P P H P R W R H T X O N
T G O D Y O A H H B T S G U I
O D G I S S R I C R U K N C
P K L Y Z Q P T E R A D S T A
A O R O C K O D L S E E P A J
Z H W K G H O U S E E J A I N
C S U O I C E R P P S T E N L
L B E R Y L E R U S B O H S T
```

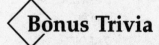

◇ Bonus Trivia

Who died for denouncing Herod?

John the Baptist (Mark 6:18–28)

173

86

Returning Exiles: Settlers of Jerusalem & Family Branches

ABDA	JOZABAD
ADAIAH	JUDAH
AHITUB	LEVI
AKKUB	MAASEIAH
AMASHAI	MATTANIAH
ASAPH	PEREZ
ATHAIAH	PETHAHIAH
BAKBUK	SALLAI
BENJAMIN	SALLU
BUNNI	SERAIAH
GABBAI	SHEMAIAH
IMMER	TALMON
JACHIN	UZZI
JEDAIAH	ZABDIEL
JOEL	

```
S V H A M A S H A I Y G F L G
K W A H I T U B J E P O G E D
P F I I V E L W U E G M A I A
E H N Z B U H P R K A O B D F
T H A M H P L E E A K N B B I
H A T I A A Z L S S I A A A A
A I T S A M I E A M G D I Z L
H A A O B R I A A S A A D H L
I D M B D A E J H A A B P A A
A E Y U H J N S N T D A J I S
H J F N E E I B I A A Z U A L
E I N N B E Z Z H L I O D M E
T Q I I H J Z O C M A J A E O
V I M M E R U T A O H U H H J
K O K U B K A B J N J Y H S N
```

Bonus Trivia

Who had 12 fingers and 12 toes in the Old Testament?

ʇuɐıƃ ∀ ɥʇɐƃ ʇɐ (ς-07:17 ʅǝnɯɐS 7)

(A giant at Gath (2 Samuel 21:20-22))

175

87

Returning Exiles: Signers of Agreement with God

ABIJAH	KADMIEL
AHIAH	MAASEIAH
AMARIAH	MAAZIAH
ANAN	MALLUCH
AZARIAH	MEREMOTH
BAANAH	MICHA
BARUCH	MIJAMIN
BILGAI	NEHEMIAH
BINNUI	OBADIAH
DANIEL	PASHUR
HARIM	REHOB
HATTUSH	REHUM
JEREMIAH	SERAIAH
JESHUA	SHEMAIAH

```
H C M F H N D I U J E S H U A
T H A N A A B A I H K I N D A
O R A R I L A G U R A O X H M
M J S R D E R L N A H J I F A
E E E U A I U I N A H A I U R
R R I H B N C B I L H L B B I
E E A S O A H M B E N N I H A
M M H A Y D E D E I I A A P H
U I Y P H H S H R M M I N M S
H A P O E E A E A D Z K I A U
E H D N R R H J T A X C Q B T
R A E A I O I E A K A B A V T
I B I M B M B M A L L U C H A
O A H C I M A Z A R I A H Q H
H E H A I A M E H S S B C X T
```

Bonus Trivia

What Bible character was the father of 88 children?

Rehoboam (28 sons and 60 daughters)
(2 Chronicles 11:21)

88

Signers of Agreement with God #2

ADIN

ADONIJAH

ANAIAH

ANATHOTH

ATER

AZGAD

AZZUR

BANI

BEBAI

BENINU

BEZAI

BIGVAI

BUNNI

ELAM

HANAN

HANANIAH

HARIPH

HASHUM

HASSHUB

HEZEKIAH

HEZIR

HOSHEA

JADDUA

MAGPIASH

NOB

PAROSH

PELAIAH

PELATIAH

ZACCUR

ZADOK

ZATTU

```
B A W W Z H A I N A N A H W D
I B U N N I A J A D D U A A H
G H E Z E K I A H E B O G M P
V P E L A T I A H E L Z C A I
A H I B E Z A I B W A A R D R
I B A N K F Z A D O K O M O A
R F E S A V I O I L S S H N H
A U N N H B A R Z H C S Z I N
P N C O I U T N E W A A N J A
E O A C B N M O A I T I I A N
L Q Y I A A U Y P T H L D H A
A T E R A Z I G U U H E A O H
I Z F N G H A R X Q Q O Z F H
A Z Z U R M H O S H E A T I K
H P C B U R H A S S H U B H R
```

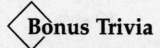

Bonus Trivia

What book records the story of Boaz?

ꓤnʇɥ

89

Fourth Things in the Bible

ADONIJAH	MONTH
ANGEL	NETHANEEL
BEAST	NOHAH
CAPTAIN	PART
CHARIOT	RIVER
CHERUB	ROW
DAY	SACAR
FACE	SEAL
FOUNDATION	SEORIM
IZRI	SHALLUM
JATHNIEL	WARD
JEKAMEAM	WATCH
KINGDOM	WHEEL
LOT	WING
MAN	YEAR
MISHMANNAH	ZECHARIAH

```
J A B O A N G E L G S E A L T
T O I R A H C G N A M X W O R
Z H M R H A M I C B D D E Y W
J E A A E A W L Q A S R C U P
W F C H E V N N E P S A O N S
T N P H O M I N O E A T F W S
Z R I H A N A R A C H E A H V
A Z A Z D R I K A M Z W A I Q
Y A D P R M I R E X H L X X N
V A D O N I J A H J L S T L M
K I N G D O M D H U G O I I O
J A T H N I E L M V L X X M N
R U N N O I T A D N U O F T T
B N E T H A N E E L Y E A R H
C H E R U B E A S T W A T C H
```

◇ Bonus Trivia

King Ahab said, "There is still one man through whom we can inquire of the Lord, but I hate him because he never prophesies anything good about me." About whom was he speaking?

Micaiah (1 Kings 22:8)

181

90

Favour (-ed)

CAUSE

CHILDREN

CLOUD

DANIEL

DECEITFUL

DEW

DUST

ESTHER

EYES

FATHERLESS

GOD

HADAD

HORN

JOB

KINE

KINGS

LAND

LIFE

LORD

LOVING

MAN

MEN

NAPHTALI

PEOPLE

PRINCE

RACHEL

RULERS

RUTH

SAUL

SIGHT

WICKED

UNDERSTANDING

YOUNG

```
A G M E C N E M T H G I S I M
S N N L L U F T I E C E D K M
G I R P S B L A N D D Q A G T
N V O O S D U O L C U R D N I
I O H E E Q Z V N A S U E I K
K L Z P L O L O A U T T K D G
E C N I R P N E P S X H C N N
T K I N E R E C H E N K I A U
B X K L H E R D T C F Q W T O
G O I N T H D H A D A D G S Y
V F J A A T L H L N V R T R F
E H M M F S I L I Q I L N E W
D R O L Z E H Q A Q G E Y D O
I P R G O D C D E W X E L N S
L U A S H R U L E R S S K U A
```

◇ Bonus Trivia

Who was Jeremiah's secretary?

Baruch (Jeremiah 32:12)

183

91

Much in the Bible

BETTER	LAND
BLOOD	LESS
BRASS	MONEY
BREAD	MORE
BUSINESS	MOVED
CATTLE	PEOPLE
CEDAR	PRAISED
CINNAMON	RAIN
CONTEMPT	RICHES
DOWRY	RUBBISH
ELDER	SEED
EVIL	SET
FOOD	SLOTHFUL
GOLD	SORROW
GOOD	SPOIL
GRIEF	STRENGTH
HEED	STUDY
HONEY	WATER
INCREASE	WICKED

```
D E V O M D N A L O I D L O G
O I C O Y S S E N I S U B Y O
O L R D E W O R R O S D E E H
L E U H S B D C A T T L E N T
B T C P S E R A O C Y E N O H
S I O S S U A C D F O O D M R
R I A I B R G R E T T E B A L
L R A B E T P M E T N O C N U
B R I T F E I R G E V I L N F
P S A R M A K Y R W O D R I H
H W G A I N C R E A S E G C T
T R E D L E N D E K C I W F O
E V G E O E V I D A E R B K L
S V L C I O S D A I C D E E S
P E O P L E G S T R E N G T H
```

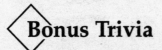

Bonus Trivia

What do diligent hands bring?

Wealth (Proverbs 10:4)

92

Much in the Bible # 2

AFFLICTION

AGAINST

ALMS

ASSURANCE

BOLD

BREAD

CONTENTION

DAMAGE

DISPLEASED

DISPUTING

EARTH

FLESH

FRUIT

GAIN

GOODS

GRASS

INCENSE

LABOUR

LEARNING

LOVE

PAIN

PATIENCE

PERPLEXED

RATHER

SERVING

SOPE

TIME

TREMBLING

TROUBLED

VEXED

WINE

WOOD

WORK

D	E	X	E	L	P	R	E	P	F	R	U	I	T	N
W	D	A	E	R	B	G	N	I	N	R	A	E	L	O
E	A	R	T	H	D	P	A	T	I	E	N	C	E	R
W	D	I	S	P	L	E	A	S	E	D	G	P	E	E
Q	E	T	R	E	M	B	L	I	N	G	O	H	M	I
F	U	C	V	Q	X	T	L	B	A	S	T	I	D	N
J	L	O	O	A	A	A	S	S	U	A	T	F	D	C
G	L	E	L	N	B	T	S	N	R	O	V	U	I	E
E	N	M	S	O	T	U	G	N	I	V	R	E	S	N
G	S	I	U	H	R	E	S	I	F	A	K	T	P	S
A	V	R	M	A	C	S	N	G	D	R	G	D	U	E
M	E	A	N	R	A	L	I	T	O	L	O	A	T	N
A	X	C	Z	R	U	R	A	W	I	O	O	A	I	I
D	E	D	G	G	A	M	P	A	W	O	D	B	N	W
O	D	A	F	F	L	I	C	T	I	O	N	S	G	T

◇ Bonus Trivia

All hard work brings a profit, but what does talk bring?

Penury, or poverty (Proverbs 10:4)

93
Pour (-ed, -eth) in the Bible

ANGER	MILK
ASHES	MONEY
BLOOD	OIL
COMPLAINT	OINTMENT
CONTEMPT	PRAYER
CURSE	RAIN
DRINK	SACRIFICES
EVIL	SOUL
FILTHINESS	SPIRIT
FOOLISHNESS	STONES
FORNICATIONS	TEARS
FURY	VIAL
GALL	WATER
GRACE	WHOREDOM
HEART	WRATH
LIVER	

```
Y B O W Q D J L O F S I L O T
H L I R V Y U S R I R C I T Z
B O N A E O F E C L A L J N G
T O T T S W O C O T E R A I N
F D M H R A R I N H T R D A Y
O R E S U T N F T I P E Y L I
O I N T C E I I E N K Y E P X
L N T O V R C R M E P A N M T
I K R N B M A C P S P R O O I
S E E E F I T A T S E P M C R
H C V S U L I S A V T H D O I
N A I H R K O V N I H R S C P
E R L F Y U N O G A L L A A S
S G E V I L S G E L F D U E G
S R G K Y W H O R E D O M X H
```

◇ **Bonus Trivia**

Who said, "I see people; they look like trees walking around."

A blind man whom Jesus healed (Mark 8:24)

94
Generation (-s), (of)

AARON	JACOB
ADAM	JOY
CHOSEN	LEVI
CROOKED	NOAH
DESOLATIONS	OLD
ESAU	PERVERSE
EVERY	PHAREZ
EVIL	REBELLIOUS
FAITHLESS	SHEM
FOUNDATIONS	STUBBORN
FOURTH	TENTH
FROWARD	TERAH
HEAVENS	THIRD
ISAAC	VIPERS
ISHMAEL	WISER

```
X B F J R Z E R A H P D C L S
W I O F E H T N E T C A A S I
P D U C O S N D L E A M H S I
N F R L A U A O O H E V I L O
E A T I H J N U R S V F W S P
S I H S H A S D R A R K U L N
O T A O N T R E A O A O E X R
H H O Y R E V E W T I V H E O
C L N V Q R V A T L I D F S B
R E E X E H R A L A E O I C B
O S D P Z D P E E Y D G N A U
O S L O O M B X P H O A A S T
K K O S R E P I V A X J M A S
E R R G R H Q L Q F W I S E R
D X A D E S O L A T I O N S M
```

191

95

Appointed in the Bible

BARLEY	NIGHTS
CAPTAIN	PLACE
CITIES	PREACHER
DAYS	PROPHETS
DEFEAT	PURIM
DESTRUCTION	RULER
DIE	SEASON
DISCIPLES	SEED
FEASTS	SHEEP
HEIR	SIGN
HERITAGE	SINGERS
HOUSE	THING
KEDESH	TIME
LAW	TWO
LEVITES	VICTUALS
MEAT	WARDS
MEN	WEEKS
MOON	YEAR

```
S N I G H T S T D L Y J R E H
G E R A E Y T A I E C P U C E
D N A I R X S E S V A L L A R
P A O S E B A M C I P A E L I
E D Y I O H E I I T T W R P T
E T E S T N F R P E A D H T A
H P N F J C B U L S I Y L W G
S S R S E N U P E E N F M O E
W H E O R A W R S S M E P T C
K A O I P E T E T N N O D H K
E G R U T H G V E S G E O I E
D Z U D S I E N V K E I I N M
E S P B S E C T I S S D S G I
S L A U T C I V S S T I Q H T
H R E H C A E R P Y E L R A B
```

Bonus Trivia

Who fell off his chair and died when he heard the ark had been stolen?

Eli (1 Samuel 4:18)

96

Ezekiel's Vision

ALTAR	IMAGE
BATTLE AX	INCENSE
BEASTS	LINEN
BONES	LOCK
BORDER	MEAT
BREATH	RAINBOW
CALDRON	ROD
CHERUB	SANCTUARY
COURT	SINEWS
DOOR	SLAIN
DRY	SWORD
ELDERS	TEMPLE
FLAX	THRESHOLD
GATE	VOICE
GLORY	WAIST
HAIR	WATCHMAN
HAND	WIFE
HOUSE	WOMEN
IDOLS	

```
H A I R B A T T L E A X C W M
R A T L A I D O L S R A Q S R
E E U H M N Y W A L B O W B D
C Y S A R W I D O R U O O N N
I W G A L E T A E M R N N D A
O E O I N X S E L D E Z A F H
V R N B A C E H S S H N M C S
G E B L N L T W O U C J H O R
N W F O P I E U I L O E C U E
J W I M R N A N A G D H T R D
E L E F I D C R L R K Y A T L
T T O S E E E O J D Y U W Q E
A B Y C N N R R O H T A E R B
G R T S K Y U C A L D R O N C
D J E W A I S T S A E B T F O
```

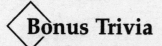

Bonus Trivia

Who killed Jonathan, Saul's son?

The Philistines (1 Chronicles 10:2)

97

More of Ezekiel's Visions

AMBER	LIGHTNING
BERYL	LION
BODIES	MAN
BRONZE	NOISE
CLOUD	OX
COALS	RIMS
CREATURES	SAPPHIRE
CRYSTAL	SPIRIT
EAGLE	STONE
EYES	THRONE
FACES	TORCHES
FEET	TUMULT
FIRE	WHEEL
FLASH	WHIRLWIND
HANDS	WINGS
LEGS	

```
O H N Z E Z N O R B W I N G S
S M I R L R M R M Z S D L P B
G M M A E H A B S L F L A S H
P B Z S A E N E A E S L E G S
L N I N R F R O L X E N O T S
J O D I E U C E K W H E E L R
N S F E T T A I B T L U M U T
Y G T A H G W H I R L W I N D
N X E R L L L I B N T D J S T
F R O E R I Y B B W O U D E I
C N Y N O D S R P L R O A I R
E V C N O F A C E S C L M D I
Y X L A T S Y R C B H C B O P
E S A P P H I R E B E L E B S
S L I G H T N I N G S Q R X J
```

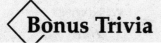

Bonus Trivia

Who owned the cattle on 1,000 hills?

God (Psalm 50:10)

98

Job's Problems & Blessings

ASHES

BILDAD

BLAMELESS

BOILS

CAMELS

CHALDEANS

DAUGHTERS

DONKEYS

DUST

ELIHU

ELIPHAZ

EVIL

FEAST

FIRE

GOD

GRIEF

HEDGE

LORD

OXEN

POTSHERD

ROBE

SABEANS

SATAN

SERVANTS

SHAVED

SHEEP

SHUNS

SONS

SWORD

TORE

UPRIGHT

UZ

VOICES

WEPT

WHIRLWIND

WIFE

WIND

ZOPHAR

F	P	U	R	S	L	W	H	I	R	L	W	I	N	D
F	E	G	G	A	N	Z	A	H	P	I	L	E	K	H
S	I	A	S	O	H	A	D	V	D	T	E	D	G	E
O	L	R	S	H	D	P	E	R	R	P	F	A	N	D
J	X	E	E	T	U	S	O	D	O	E	I	D	S	G
S	N	E	M	E	U	N	T	Z	L	W	W	L	H	E
Y	E	W	N	A	I	P	S	N	G	A	S	I	A	Y
E	L	I	H	U	C	S	R	S	A	R	H	B	V	P
K	G	N	G	S	W	G	E	I	A	V	I	C	E	O
N	D	D	L	U	D	F	A	H	G	T	R	E	D	T
O	L	I	Z	U	E	R	O	T	S	H	A	E	F	S
D	O	I	S	N	A	E	B	A	S	A	T	N	S	H
B	F	T	V	F	S	N	O	S	R	O	B	E	G	E
B	L	A	M	E	L	E	S	S	H	E	E	P	B	R
S	E	C	I	O	V	S	R	E	T	H	G	U	A	D

◇ Bonus Trivia

Where was Paul when he had his hair cut off?

Cenchrea (Acts 18:18)

199

99
Beginning in the Bible

ABIB
ALPHA
BETHEL
CREATION
DAYS
DISCIPLES
EARTH
ELDEST
FIRSTBORN
GALILEE
GENERATIONS
GOSPEL
HARVEST
HEAVENS
JERUSALEM
KNOWLEDGE
MIRACLES
MONTHS
MOSES
REIGN
REUBEN
REVENGES
SHOOTING
SIN
SINK
SORROWS
SUPPLICATIONS
WATCH
WAY
WISDOM
WORD
WORLD
YEAR

```
Q R G E N E R A T I O N S D H
U B G O S P E L O S W O R L D
T S E L C A R I M U W O R D O
S I N Y E G D E L W O N K C D
E W S R A E Y S O R R O W S A
V I P P J E R U S A L E M A Y
R S N O I T A C I L P P U S S
A D M O N T H S H O O T I N G
H O A B I B N R O B T S R I F
R M O S E S G A L I L E E E L
R E V E N G E S U E U A L W E
S E L P I C S I D B H L D A H
Y A W N O I T A E R C P E T T
R E I G N L K N I S O H S C E
S N E V A E H T R A E A T H B
```

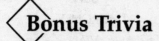

Bonus Trivia

What is more valuable than rubies?

Wisdom (Proverbs 8:11)

100

Who Beheld What?

ANGEL	JOSES
BEAST	LABAN
BRASS	LINEN
CITY	LOT
CLOTHES	MAID
DANIEL	MANASSEH
DEVOTIONS	MOUNTAINS
DISCIPLES	PEOPLE
EGYPTIANS	PLACE
ENEMIES	PLAIN
GLORY	SATAN
HORN	SEPULCHRE
HORSE	SINEWS
JACOB	SLAIN
JEREMIAH	SUN
JESUS	THRONES
JOB	VIAL
JOHN	WINGS
JORDAN	WOMEN

```
E D M O U N T A I N S L A I N
R H M N R O H A J U J A C O B
H X T A J Y N O S D E I T O L
C O H A I G R E E L C V N I X
L S R Q E D J N P G L O R Y J
U I O L A T E O J W O M E N O
P N N N R M E G Y P T I A N S
E E E Y I P Y Q L Q H S P E E
S W S E L W T S U N E N I L S
R S S A R B I U Z B S G N I W
O K C J O B C L L E I N A D B
H E S S A N A M Q L A B A N E
N I A L P D I S C I P L E S A
G F J E R E M I A H N A T A S
N H O J Y S N O I T O V E D T
```

◇ Bonus Trivia

If a cheerful heart is good medicine, what does a crushed spirit do?

Dry up the bones (Proverbs 17:22)

101
People in Canaan
(Genesis 36)

ACHBOR	HORI
ADAH	HUSHAM
AHOLIBAMAH	MANAHATH
AKAN	MASREKAH
ALVAN	MATRED
BAALHANAN	MEHETABEL
BEDAD	MOAB
BELA	ONAM
BEOR	SAMLAH
DINHABAH	SAUL OF REHOBOTH
DISHON	SHEPHO
ESAU	SHOBAL
EZER	TIMNA
HADAD	ZAVAAN
HEMAM	ZIBEON

```
A M A T R E D H T A H A N A M
A H H I Y A J D I S H O N A A
M L O Z U A U A E Y H N N R S
E S H L Z I A L V A N O E E R
H I O Z I H S J E M I Z R R E
E H H Z B B E D A D E O P O K
T A P L E E A O A A T H E B A
A B E N O L I M S D I O U H H
B A H A N A M O A A L O V C E
E H S A V I O A M H U S H A M
L N H V R O E B L T I M N A H
I I O A K A N I A D A H T H I
S D B Z I O R Z H E M A M X Y
H S A U L O F R E H O B O T H
I Z L X H J N A N A H L A A B
```

◇ **Bonus Trivia**

Finish the sentence, "Ye have not yet resisted unto blood—"

"striving against sin." (Hebrews 12:4)

102

Pharaoh's Prophetic Dream
(Genesis 41)

BAKER	LAND
CHARIOT	LINEN
CORN	MAGICIANS
DISCREET	PERISH
DREAMS	PHARAOH
FAMINE	PLENTY
FED	RIVER
FOOD	RULER
GATHER	SEVEN
GOD	STALK
GOLD	STORE
GOOD EARS	THIN EARS
HANGED	WIND
INTERPRET	WISE
KINE	YEARS

```
I  L  I  N  E  N  I  O  R  E  H  T  A  G  Y
C  N  G  O  O  D  E  A  R  S  I  O  U  E  X
H  O  T  T  E  E  R  C  S  I  D  I  A  W  E
A  O  P  E  P  L  E  N  T  Y  I  R  N  B  Q
R  P  H  A  R  A  O  H  I  Y  S  E  V  E  N
I  H  W  Q  U  P  T  H  I  N  E  A  R  S  I
O  X  Q  U  I  D  R  E  A  M  S  W  I  S  E
T  X  K  L  A  T  S  E  A  A  T  G  O  L  D
H  A  N  G  E  D  O  X  T  G  O  O  W  E  W
S  N  R  O  C  O  S  W  O  I  R  I  A  N  I
I  O  U  R  R  O  A  D  O  C  E  D  I  I  N
R  U  L  E  R  F  I  X  U  I  N  N  N  M  D
E  A  V  K  Q  U  D  D  K  A  K  O  P  A  I
P  I  P  A  P  E  G  O  B  N  W  W  I  F  L
R  I  B  B  F  W  Q  G  X  S  K  I  N  E  J
```

◇ **Bonus Trivia**

Who said, "The most High dwelleth not in temples made with hands"?

Stephen (Acts 7:48)

103

The Tower of Babel
(Genesis 11)

ABROAD	LANGUAGE
BABEL	LORD
BEHOLD	MORTER
BRICK	NAME
BUILDED	NOTHING
CHILDREN	ONE
CITY	PEOPLE
CONFOUND	PLAIN
DWELT	SCATTERED
EARTH	SHINAR
EAST	SLIME
FACE	SPEECH
HEAVEN	STONE
IMAGINED	TOWER
JOURNEYED	UNDERSTAND

```
U I M A G I N E D H J O N E L
A N H T R A E L O V C J M M O
C N D A N L Q U F A C E H H R
O I A E P N O T H I N G E N D
N A M O R T E R M E A A Y P E
F L E G N S T A R I V E N D S
O P M B I X T D Q E O R N W D
U D T A R M L A N G U A G E E
N L O T I I M L N O P N I L R
D O W Q H I C X E D S I T T E
J H E C M J L K O B I H Q N T
O E R Q U S T O N E A S T A T
Q B I J K D E D L I U B W M A
J O U R N E Y E D I L O V E C
C I T Y A B R O A D E M I L S
```

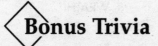

Bonus Trivia

Who asked, "Am I my brother's keeper"?

Cain (Genesis 4:9)

104

Joseph's Temptation
(Genesis 39)

BLESSING

BREAD

EGYPT

EYES

FIELD

FLED

GARMENT

GOD

HEBREW

HOUSE

ISHMAELITES

JOSEPH

KEEPER

LIE WITH ME

LORD

MASTER

MASTER'S WIFE

MERCY

MOCK

OVERSEER

POTIPHAR

PRISON

PRISONERS

PROSPER

SERVANT

VOICE

WICKEDNESS

WRATH

```
P R I S O N E R S E R V A N T
M O L I E W I T H M E O H M B
M V T O L M A S T E R I O A L
E E L I X H P N L O V C B S E
R R W G P H A R O A H E A T S
C S E O Y H E L O S Y O U E S
Y E R D H S A H X S I W E R I
Y E B D U T H R P W P R A S N
I R E O A N F S I E W E P W G
I S H M A E L I T E S B R I V
T H O D F M E E Y M U O D F S
P T I A I R D E L O R D J E J
Y A S E E A S L C C L O T Y Q
G R I R L G I Y A K E E P E R
E W H B D S S E N D E K C I W
```

◇ **Bonus Trivia**

Of whom was it said, when he died at the age of one hundred and twenty, "His eye was not dim, nor his natural force abated"?

Moses (Deuteronomy 34:7)

105

Joseph Entertains His Brothers

(Genesis 43)

AFRAID

ALMONDS

BENJAMIN

BIRTHRIGHT

BOWED

BREAD

BROTHER

CHAMBER

EGYPTIANS

FAMINE

FATHER

FOOD

GOD

GRACIOUS

HEBREWS

HONEY

ISRAEL

JOSEPH

JUDAH

MERRY

MONEY

MYRRH

OBEISANCE

PEACE

SACKS

SERVANT

SIMEON

SPICES

TREASURE

WEPT

```
B E N J A M I N O H A D U J M
O J M M T M N O E M I S G Y E
S B O W E D B R O T H E R X R
K I E J I L W X Q U R R A J R
C R N I R R E B M A H C C O Y
A T I S S P I C E S J I S X
S H M R E A T M O N E Y O E G
N R A A R F N H I Y A M U P O
A I F E V O M C H X Q U S H D
I G R L A O T R E A S U R E T
T H R M N D J M B I D T O D A
P T R E T Y T M R A F R A I D
Y H O N E Y H I E P E A C E A
G O F A T H E R W A T W O M A
E F A I T H B S S D N O M L A
```

Bonus Trivia

Complete the prayer, "Create in me a clean heart, O God—"

"and renew a right spirit within me."
(Psalm 51:10)

106

A Bride for Isaac
(Genesis 24)

ABRAHAM	MASTER
ANGEL	OATH
BETHUEL	PITCHER
BRACELETS	PROSPER
CAMELS	RAIMENT
CANAANITES	REBEKAH
DAUGHTER	SARAH
DRINK	SERVANT
EARRING	SILVER
FLOCKS	VAIL
GOLD	VIRGIN
ISAAC	WATER
JEWELS	WELL
KINDRED	WIFE
LABAN	WOMEN

```
C A M E L S I O P R O S P E R
W A E T I L O V G N I R R A E
S B N N J M A C W A T E R M L
I E D A I S A A R E B E K A H
L T L V A B R A H A M I B I G
V H O R Q N U S Q U X A I O U
E U G E I A I I K I N D R E D
R E T S A M F T R A I M E N T
I L O W E L L W E T E H J M M
L I A V O S O M A S A S H J X
E X I T N L C O T R K N I R D
G I V E N E K D A U G H T E R
N A M E W W S S W N I G R I V
A O A T H E B R A C E L E T S
W I F E X J W A R E H C T I P
```

Bonus Trivia

Finish Christ's saying, "Suffer the little children—"

"to come unto me, and forbid them not: for of such is the kingdom of God." (Mark 10:14)

107

The Burning Bush
(Exodus 3)

ABRAHAM	ISAAC
BURNED	JACOB
BUSH	JETHRO
CHILDREN	JEWELS
CONSUMED	LAND
DAUGHTERS	LORD
DELIVER	MEMORIAL
EGYPT	MILK
FIRE	MOSES
GOLD	NAME
GROUND	PHARAOH
HOLY	RAIMENT
HONEY	SHOES
HOREB	SILVER
I AM	SONS

```
Z S I L V E R H O A R A H P M
E U D A U G H T E R S I O O M
G U L B U R N E D M S Z S Q J
Y H O N E Y R E V I L E D E M
P O U F I R E J M L S Q W Z Y
T L E M A N I O Q K Q E U M S
Z A L O O K G O S A L L D D T
M I O M S S D B T S U I P E K
A R R T C O N S U M E D H T Z
H O D U M N A Z X S H O E S T
A M P Q B S L I A M H O R E B
R E S O W R R O G R O U N D V
B M C R A I M E N T L O V E Y
A A I S A A C I O U Y G O L D
J E T H R O N N E R D L I H C
```

◇ Bonus Trivia

Who said, "I am he that liveth, and was
dead; and, behold, I am alive for evermore"?

Christ (Revelation 1:18)

217

108

The Flood
(Genesis 6-8)

ALTAR	GOPHER WOOD
ARARAT	GRACE
ARK	HAM
BEAST	JAPHETH
CATTLE	MOUNTAINS
COVENANT	MULTIPLY
CUBITS	NOAH
DESTROY	OLIVE LEAF
DOVE	RAVEN
EARTH	SHEM
FLESH	SMITE
FORTY DAYS	WATERS
FORTY NIGHTS	WICKEDNESS
FOWL	WIFE
GIANTS	WINDOW

```
A F B E A S T T N A N E V O C
G O P H E R W O O D A B Q D A
I R W W A T E R S X U Z E E T
A T Y I R A V E N B C C W S T
N Y L O T A L T A R A B C T L
T N P H H S I L U R R Q E R E
S I I S O W S Z G I K F E O N
M G T E M A H E I U I V S Y T
I H L L I X E Z N W O Q T U O
T T U F Q U M T O D Z O I L W
E S M H I Y A J A R E M B W O
I O J A P H E T H R I K U O D
O L I V E L E A F I A E C F N
I S N I A T N U O M I R W I I
F O R T Y D A Y S I O U A I W
```

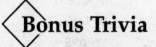

Bonus Trivia

Finish the proverb, "Whom the Lord
loveth—"

"he correcteth." (Proverbs 3:12)

109

Creation
(Genesis 1)

BEAST	FRUIT
BEGINNING	GOD
BLESSED	HEAVEN
CATTLE	HERB
CREATED	IMAGE
CREATURE	LIGHT
DARKNESS	MALE
DAY	MULTIPLY
DOMINION	NIGHT
DRY LAND	SEAS
EARTH	SEASONS
FEMALE	VOID
FIRMAMENT	WATERS
FISH	WHALES
FOWL	YEARS

```
G O D I L U S I D E S S E L B
F I P X I W J A X N E V A E H
O R U H I M A G E S I O G A C
W S U S H I Y A J S I I X R A
L E N I G H T D M E N D H T T
A A F F T H E U T N I O U H T
W S A I U T L N I K H I Y A L
S O I W A T E N S R E T A W E
R N I E I M G I N A X Y H Z K
A S R P A Y U Y A D E A Z J I
E C L M X Y Q D N A L Y R D O
Y Y R I F E M A L E A B S X Y
L I G H T L I F S I M X R Q U
F D O M I N I O N T T S A E B
C R E A T U R E A R W Q U R H
```

◇ Bonus Trivia

Who said, "The half was not told me," and concerning whom?

The queen of Sheba, concerning Solomon's wisdom and splendor (1 Kings 10:7)

110

Plagues
(Exodus 7-12)

AARON
BLOOD
BOILS
DARKNESS
DEATH
EARTH
EGYPTIANS
ENCHANTMENTS
FIRSTBORN
FLAX
FROGS
GOD
HAIL
HEART
HEBREWS

LAMB
LOCUSTS
LORD
MAGICIANS
MOSES
PASSOVER
PHARAOH
ROD
SACRIFICES
SERPENTS
SMITE
SWARMS OF FLIES
THUNDER
WIND

```
E B L O O D S N A I C I G A M
A N X S E C I F I R C A S D O
R F C I E G Y P T I A N S A S
T I H H A T H U N D E R W R E
H R P P A S S O V E R S E K S
S S N I A N H H I Y A T R N E
K T E Y R X T R N L X N B E T
Q B K Y O J A M O J A E E S I
O O C B N X E R E D L P H S M
M R I P M Y D I S N F R O G S
S N R Z L A X Y L O T E A T S
R Y T W I J L W I N D S G O D
V X S W A R M S O F F L I E S
I L O V H I O M B H E A R T P
L O C U S T S I H O A R A H P
```

◇ **Bonus Trivia**

Fill out the verse, "In thy presence —;
at thy right hand —"

(Psalm 16:11)
"is fulness of joy; at thy right hand
there are pleasures for evermore."

111
Character of God

COMFORTER

COMPASSIONATE

COUNSELOR

DELIVERER

FATHER

FORTRESS

FRIEND

HOPE

INTERCEDER

JOY

LIFE

LIGHT

LOVE

MERCIFUL

MIRACLE WORKER

ROCK

SAVIOR

SHIELD

TRUTH

VICTOR

```
S A V I O R T G R C R D E P E
T S B K H S H I E L D T Q R C
U J C H R D C E K X A W A F O
B O N I O K M O R N I S H E M
R R E H T A F Y O J D M T C F
C O J S C S T I W N U I U R O
A L A S I F S V E D J P R E R
B E M O V S L I L I G H T R T
A S P O A Z R W C E Q M R E E
B N J P X F V L A V C F L V R
N U M S S E R T R O F I O I R
W O M U Y M T T I L F A I L O
C C E P O H E E M E A R B E T
R E D E C R E T N I I C A D Y
F M E R C I F U L C O M M U N
```

Bonus Trivia

Complete Christ's questions, "Is not the life more than meat—"

"and the body than raiment?" (Matthew 6:25)

112

Biblical Churches

ANTIOCH

ATHENS

BEREA

COLOSSE

CORINTH

DERBE

EPHESUS

GALATIA

ICONIUM

JERUSALEM

LAODICEA

LYSTRA

PHILADELPHIA

PHILIPPI

ROME

SARDIS

SMYRNA

THESSALONICA

TROAS

```
P H A I T A L A G E H I S C B
H S C O R I N T H S T A I I A
I U M R E T Y N H S A C D D E
L O N E I H E R D O B I R M B
I G K O L D S U A L S N A U A
P E C Q A A U O E O S O S I Y
P H B V E H S H M C E L L N L
I W L R C N E U O N H A A O A
B U Y L E M H M R A T S Z C N
A T S H J D P I Q E P S U I R
I N T G I Z E W Y U J E R O Y
T A R R O N E X M M F H E A M
E R A E R E B S A O R T J L S
H Y A T A E C I D O A L R A P
T I A I H P L E D A L I H P H
```

Bonus Trivia

Who said, "Let God be true, but every man a liar"?

113

Crown

ANOINTING OIL

BEAUTIFUL

CORRUPTIBLE

ENDURE

FALLEN

FLOURISH

GIVEN

GLORY

GOLD

GOLDEN

GOLDEN PLATE

GREAT

HEAD

HOLY

KINGS

LIFE

MANY

OLD MEN

PRIDE

REJOICING

RIGHTEOUSNESS

ROYAL

STONES

THORNS

TWELVE STARS

VIRTUOUS WOMEN

WISE

```
I  Y  N  A  M  S  E  J  W  G  I  P  N  S  O
C  H  R  D  T  B  F  K  H  R  R  O  E  N  L
D  B  O  O  P  R  I  D  E  E  G  N  L  R  D
L  E  Y  L  L  I  L  K  A  A  O  E  L  O  M
I  T  A  C  Y  G  O  L  D  T  L  M  A  H  E
O  A  L  O  N  H  I  R  S  I  D  O  F  T  N
G  L  S  R  A  T  S  E  V  L  E  W  T  U  L
N  P  L  R  C  E  Q  J  D  G  N  S  H  V  U
I  N  J  U  F  O  S  O  K  D  B  U  S  E  F
T  E  E  P  E  U  T  I  H  H  F  O  I  A  I
N  D  D  T  R  S  E  C  W  T  A  U  R  G  T
I  L  P  I  U  N  K  I  P  O  L  T  U  I  U
O  O  K  B  D  E  T  N  Q  M  N  R  O  V  A
N  G  R  L  N  S  S  G  N  I  K  I  L  E  E
A  N  O  E  E  S  A  I  V  W  J  V  F  N  B
```

Bonus Trivia

Who asked, "Is there no balm in Gilead; is there no physician there?"

Jeremiah (Jeremiah 8:22)

114
The Tongue

ARROW

BLASPHEME

BLESSING

BRAG

BRIDLETH

CANNOT BE TAMED

CONFESS

CURSE

DEADLY POISON

DECEITFUL

DEFILETH

FAIL

FALSE

FIRE

FLATTERETH

GRUDGE

LAPPETH

LYING

NAUGHTY

PEN

PRAISE

PRAY

SCOURGE

SING

SLANDER

SLOW

SOFT

STAMMERING

SWEAR

UTTER

WORLD OF EVIL

```
S C B M I A F A L G P I N Y L
P A I S L A N D E R G Y N P W
N R E O U H C F L H T O D O O
W U M F F T R A E W S E R B L
O C E T T E V I Y I M L L N S
R H H Y I P J L O A D E E C T
R T P T E P G P T O S S O P A
A E S H C A Y E F S I U J L M
S L A G E L B E I A R K C O M
S I L U D T V N R G R U D G E
E F B A O I G P E N R V Z S R
F E E N L Y I N G S B Y I G I
N D N K W U T T E R L N A A N
O A B R I D L E T H G A W R G
C P E H T E R E T T A L F B P
```

Bonus Trivia

Who spoke of the time "when the morning stars sang together, and all the sons of God shouted for joy"?

The Lord, to Job (Job 38:7)

115

Psalm 66

BEHOLD
BLESS
COME
CRIED
DECLARE
EXTOLLED
FEAR
FIRE
FLOOD
GLORIOUS
GREATNESS
HEAR
HEARD
HEART
JOYFUL NOISE
MERCY
OFFER
POWER
PRAISE
PRAYER
PROVED
REJOICE
RULETH
SEA
SING FORTH
SOUL
SUBMIT
SUFFERETH
VOICE
VOWS
WATER
WEALTHY PLACE
WORKS
WORSHIP

```
H T R O F G N I S A I V B J S
R A E F Y Y L U O S N W Z O S
E K J O C I F C R I E D F Y E
S H O S R F M O R A R F G F N
I E I K E E R I L U E P L U T
A A C R M N T T L R W S O L A
R R E O H S H E U H O S R N E
P T C W N Y T R E J P E I O R
H U I Q P H E A V P U L O I G
D E E L X T R L T I M B U S P
R M A S A F Z C B H Q I S E R
A C I W L V O E P S U T W C A
E X T O L L E D E R I F M I Y
H L O V I C D E V O R P N O E
B D L O H E B P I W C A A V R
```

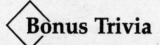

Bonus Trivia

Who asked, "Should such a man as I flee?"

Nehemiah (Nehemiah 6:11)

116

Fire

ASHES

BREASTPLATE

BRIGHT

BRIMSTONE

BURNT SACRIFICE

CHARIOT

CONSUMING

DEVOURING

ETERNAL

FLAME

FURNACE

HEARTH

HORSES

KINDLED

LAKE

MELTING

OFFERING

PILLAR

RAINED

REFINERS

RESERVED UNTO

REVEALED

ROAST

SIGN

SMOKE

TORCH

TRIED

VIOLENCE

WALL

WRATH

```
G L C C H T A R W Y M F O Y B
N G L H S R E N I F E R Q U S
I N B A C I N E L L I E R C P
T I O R W E F G K O C N O H D
L R U I P D J L I A T K T E E
E U G O I E K O M S L F N A L
M O K T L R S G A E H I U R D
T V I O L E N C E S A B D T N
S E H S A I R H C R O T E H I
K D I B R I M S T O N E V U K
P R M E F P J O T H G I R B E
A C F I Y B D E L A E V E R M
R F C O N S U M I N G U S P A
O E T A L P T S A E R B E Y L
I Z L A N R E T E C A N R U F
```

Bonus Trivia

Who said, "One thing I know, that, whereas I was blind, now I see"?

The man born blind whom Christ healed (John 9:25)

235

117

In the Wilderness

ABODE

ANGER

BAPTIZE

BORN

BREAD

DIE

DRY

DWELT

EDGE

FACE

FED YOU

FLED

FLEEING

FURY

GRACE

GREAT

HABITATIONS

HEATH

LED

MANNA

MARCH

OVERTHROWN

PIT

PLAGUES

PREACHING

RAN

SEEK

SLAY

SUSTAIN

SWORD

TARRY

TEMPTATION

TENT

TERRIBLE

THIRSTY

THORNS

VOICE THAT CRIETH

WANDER

WASTE

WAY

WEARY

WIND

WRATH

```
T F E Z I T P A B T Y R R A T
W L L C Y A L S E U G A L P E
E I E E A F Y R E D N A W H N
A T N W E R R F L E D Y I T T
R E T D D I G E S V K T R A N
Y D Y N B D N D N B N S E E W
R O Q L R I I G O O V R G H O
U B E O A W H E I R G I N V R
F A W T O A C T T N H H A T H
G S S V L S A S A E T T M E T
D U N E S T E M T V A Z A C R
S B D R P E R A I F R M R A E
A Z A M O O P N B B W X C F V
D A E R B H I N A R Q M H W O
H T E I R C T A H T E C I O V
```

◇ **Bonus Trivia**

What is the first part of the sentence
ending "loadeth us with benefits"?

"Blessed be the Lord, who daily loadeth us
with benefits." (Psalm 68:19)

118

The Sea

ABUNDANCE	NET
BRASEN	OVERFLOW
CALM	OVERWHELMED
CAST	RAGING
CHANNELS	RED
COAST	ROAR
COVER	SALT
DEPTHS	SAND
DROWNED	SHORE
EDGE	SIDE
FISH	SORROW
FISHES	STRENGTH
GLASS	TEMPEST
GREAT	TEMPESTUOUS
HAVEN	TROUBLED
HEART	UTTERMOST
HINDER	WALKING
ISLES	WATERS
LOOK TOWARD	WAVES
MIDST	WIDE
MOLTEN	

```
T S A O C E N A D N U B A L
R E V O C S D E L B U O R T O
L M U N R W O R R O S N E T O
D T H E P T S O M R E T T U K
E R T V F R S V D D V S G D T
N A J A I A L E E B A P R E O
W E V H S G E R P C W O M M W
O H F H H I N F T M A P W L A
R W O B T N N L H R E A S E R
D R I U G G A O S L T D H D
E R E D N I H W T K P G N W P
F I S H E S C U I N E S A R B
W T A E R G O N V D U A S E O
M I D S T U G Q I C A L M V K
G L A S S E L S I N E T L O M
```

◇ **Bonus Trivia**

Who said, "My punishment is greater than I can bear"?

Cain (Genesis 4:13)

119

Offerings

ATONEMENT	MEAT
BLOOD	MEMORIAL
BRASS	PASSOVER
BULLOCK	PEACE
BURNT	PEOPLES
DRINK	PIGEON
FIELDS	SACRIFICE
FIRE	SHEEP
FREE	SILVER
FREEWILL	SIN
GOAT	SWEET SAVOUR
GOLD	THANK
HEAVE	TRESPASS
JEALOUSY	TURTLEDOVE
LAMB	VOLUNTARY
LORDS	WAVE
MEAL	WILLING

```
D F S S A P S E R T R B E C T
S L I J Y R A T N U L O V H I
I H O E R F E R O S M E A L B
N O E G I P U V I U V N W P L
P C T E H B A L A O K E J A O
E K N N P S V S D E C S I Q O
O L E V T E Z E S I H R T U D
P L M E R S L A F O O N D Y W
L I E F K T D I I M V A F S I
E W N L R C R L E C A E P U L
S E O U V C O M E E S D R O L
C E T T A E M L F I R X C L I
B R A S S Q U I L I F F A A N
I F O C M B R W N U Z M O E G
A W G I O E M K O V B T A J Y
```

Bonus Trivia

Who wrote, "There is one God, and one mediator between God and men, the man Christ Jesus"?

120

Virtues & Sins

ADULTERY	LOVE
DEFILE	LUST
DRUNKEN	MEEK
ENVY	PEACE
FAITH	REVELRY
FRUIT	SEDITION
GENTLE	SORCERY
GOODNESS	SPIRIT
HATE	STRIFE
HERESY	TEMPERANCE
IDOLATRY	UNCLEAN
JEALOUSY	VAIN GLORY
JOY	WALK
KILLING	WAVER
LEWD	WRATH
LONGSUFFERING	

```
M J O Y R E T L U D A B K T S
E D K S U Y R E C R O S I W L
E S S E N D O O G E N T L E E
K T E R C T A H N B L D L A W
Y R D E L S F W I K D M I N D
E I I H E U E A R E E P N V M
C F T T A L O V E F F C G Y Y
N E I C N H M E F A I T H R R
A K O D T I U R F J L G H L T
R L N A F L T A U P E A C E A
E A R I P I R N S N O O I V L
P W H C R S T I G E T A H E O
M Y D I A E E K N E K N U R D
E C P T J E A L O U S Y A S I
T S L V A I N G L O R Y V N E
```

Bonus Trivia

Who said, "Follow me, and I will make you fishers of men"? To whom?

Christ, to Peter and Andrew (Matthew 4:19)

121

Heavenly Hosts

ANGEL	HEAVEN
ARCHANGEL	HOSTS
BATTLE	INVISIBLE
BEAUTY	JOYFUL
BENEVOLENT	LOVE
BLESSED	MICHAEL
CELESTIAL	MINISTERING
CHERUB	NEAR
CHOIR	NEWS
ETERNAL	PEACE
GABRIEL	PROTECT
GENTLE	PURE
GUARDIAN	SING
GUIDE	SPIRIT
HALO	SWEET
HARP	WINGS

```
A R C H A N G E L E A H C I M
L A H S W E N U E W I E H H I
U T O L A H I N I R R A E N N
F E I A F K S N R D J V R L I
Y E R I I G G O B S E E U A S
O W C T H S E C A E P N B N T
J S T S O H M P G T L C I R E
B E N E V O L E N T S T L E R
P L E L B I S I V N I D N T I
H T D E S S E L B U A E H E N
R T E C J L L N A I D R A U G
A A A N G E L O V Y B G R N S
E B S P I R I T V A F H P O H
A B D Y T U A E B E N I V E D
L R I U E P R O T E C T M A S
```

Bonus Trivia

Who wrote, "Then shall we know, if we follow on to know the Lord"?

Hosea (Hosea 6:3)

245

122
Family of Esau

ADAH

AHOLIBAMAH

AMALEK

ANAH

BASHEMATH

ELON

ELIPHAZ

ESAU

GATAM

ISHMAEL

JAALAM

JEUSH

KENAZ

KORAH

MIZZAH

NAHATH

NEBAJOTH

OMAR

REUEL

SHAMMAH

TEMAN

TIMNA

ZEPHO

ZERAH

ZIBEON

```
A F J E U S H A N M I T Y B K
Q H V D B P H N C T E E L O N
E U O M A R Z A T K D M R X Y
S Q H L K H H H G A T A M M H
A A P I I M A H A F H N J K N
U R E F H B D A Z T Q A D A E
E Y Z J A Y A A A G A Z H D B
L E U E R P G M K L M A K X A
I B H T K V E F A X T Z A K J
P L L E F H R M Q H Z C K H O
H H N G S U N B M A F J E K T
A A K A F U B W W R H S L B H
Z I B E O N Q D F E M C A I S
U S K Z P V P H A Z Z I M M X
I S H M A E L E H A M M A H S
```

◇ Bonus Trivia

Complete Christ's saying, "A man's life consisteth not—"

"in the abundance of the things which he possesseth." (Luke 12:15)

247

123

Critters

APE (1 KINGS 10:22)

ASP (ISAIAH 11:8)

BEAR (DANIEL 7)

CAMEL (GENESIS 12:16)

CATTLE (GENESIS 47:17)

COCK (JOHN 13:38)

DOGS (1 KINGS 14:11)

DOVE (MATTHEW 10:16)

EAGLE (EXODUS 19:4)

FROG (EXODUS 8:4)

HEIFER (GENESIS 15:9)

HEN (MATTHEW 23:37)

HORSE (REVELATION 6:8)

LAMB (EXODUS 29:39)

LEOPARD (DANIEL 7)

LION (DANIEL 7)

OSTRICH (JOB 39:13)

OWL (ISAIAH 43:20)

PARTRIDGE (JEREMIAH 17:11)

PEACOCK (JOB 39:13)

PIGEONS (LEVITICUS 1:14)

QUAILS (EXODUS 16:13)

RAVEN (GENESIS 8:7)

SERPENT (GENESIS 3:4)

SPARROW (PSALM 84:3)

SPIDER (PROVERBS 30:28)

STORK (PSALM 104:17)

SWALLOW (PSALM 84:3)

TURTLEDOVES (LEVITICUS 1:14)

VULTURES (ISAIAH 34:15)

```
S E R P E N T C S N O E G I P
L G A F E W O A F S C O W E A
I K V F E A W I A L R Q S S R
A I E I X O C X L F W R T F T
U A N B L O F O N R O O V A R
Q S M L P R S G C H R O N U I
Q A A S C T C N I K R O C U D
L W A S R A E L E M A C X R G
S N F I E Z T R G L P K A P E
P E C Y G R R T E D S P A O R
I H T M N D U A L T O V A K E
D N N V B S O T B E K V E A F
E L G A E F G N L H I C E N I
R K E G A M B O B U C N O F E
N U T U R T L E D O V E S C H
```

Bonus Trivia

Who wrote, "The soul that sinneth, it shall die"?

Ezekiel (Ezekiel 18:20)

124

Women in the Bible

ABI	JOANNA
APPHIA	JUDITH
BILHAH	LO-RUHAMAH
CHLOE	MARTHA
CLAUDIA	MARY
COZBI	MARY MAGADALENE
DEBORAH	MEHETABEL
DINAH	MICHAL
DRUSILLA	MIRIAM
ELISABETH	NAAMAH
EVE	RUTH
HAGAR	SARAH
JAEL	SYNTYCHE
JEHOSHEBA	VASHTI
JEZEBEL	ZIPPORAH

```
M E H E T A B E L X R U T H J J
I A C O Z B I D L B S M E A A
R I R L H U L W O S Y A Q R E
I H Z Y A S H M R P N R J O L
A P P G M G A J U P T T L P E
M P O A A A H R H K Y H A P B
Q A R G A M G X A F C A H I E
T Y F A N C S D M H H V C Z Z
D R U S I L L A A T E H I C E
E I Z N A T H A H L J X M H J
B R N U R L H P U C E K F L O
O B P A X D T S Q D G N U O A
R X G A H T E B A S I L E E N
A A A B Z Z N X W V Y A V X N
H H T I D U J E H O S H E B A
```

251

125

Jesus' Teachings

ANGER	LOVE
BIRTH	MIND
BLESSINGS	NEIGHBOR
DISCIPLESHIP	OBEY
ENEMIES	PEACE
FAITH	POSSESSIONS
FASTING	PRAYER
FEAR	PROMISES
FORGIVENESS	PURE
FREEDOM	REPENTANCE
FUTURE	REST
GIVE	RESURRECTION
GOD	REWARDS
GOOD	SABBATH
GREATNESS	SERVE
HAPPINESS	SIN
HEART	SOUL
HEAVEN	WEALTH
LAW	WORSHIP
LIFE	

```
S O U L F G F A S T I N G A P
S R E S U R R E C T I O N H E
E E F G T E E A A Y D G I T P
N Y R I U A E C E R E E S I U
I A J V R T D B I R T H H A R
P R E E N O L O V E S F F E
P P C E E M E T S E U L S R
A J N V O S Y S P L E A C A E
H P A E G S E S P I H S R O W
S E T F O R G I V E N E S S A
H A N I O H C N E I G H B O R
E C E L D S A G W E A L T H D
A E P M I N D S A B B A T H S
R L E D P O S S E S S I O N S
T P R O M I S E S E I M E N E
```

Bonus Trivia

Complete this quotation from Habakkuk:
"The earth shall be filled with the knowledge of the glory of the Lord—"

"as the waters cover the sea." (Habakkuk 2:14)

126

Miracles

ANGEL	LIFE
APOSTLES	LIONS
BLIND	MOSES
BLOOD	PALSY
BOIL	PAUL
CHILD	PETER
CLEANSE	PHILIP
DANIEL	RAIN
DARK	RAISE
DEMONS	RED
ELISHA	RIVER
FLY	ROCK
FREELY	ROD
FROG	SAMUEL
GIVE	SEA
HAIL	SERPENT
HEAL	SEVENTY-TWO
ISAIAH	SHADOW
JERICHO	SIGNS
JORDAN	STRENGTH
JOSHUA	WALK
LAME	WALL
LEPER	WATER
LICE	WONDERS

P	S	E	A	T	N	E	P	R	E	S	C	K	E	B
R	E	D	Y	J	R	O	D	O	D	O	O	L	B	L
O	A	L	S	E	L	T	S	O	P	A	P	A	O	I
C	F	A	T	J	O	Y	P	A	U	L	N	W	I	N
K	E	E	I	S	A	I	A	H	S	N	O	I	L	D
S	P	H	I	L	I	P	S	R	E	T	A	W	E	E
T	A	C	G	E	M	O	S	E	S	A	M	U	E	L
R	E	J	I	P	J	O	R	D	A	N	G	C	W	I
E	S	E	V	E	N	T	Y	T	W	O	I	O	N	S
N	R	R	E	R	I	V	E	R	R	L	D	I	N	H
G	E	I	L	P	R	M	E	F	A	A	A	G	A	A
T	D	C	L	E	A	N	S	E	H	R	I	I	C	N
H	N	H	A	L	I	F	E	S	Y	S	L	A	P	G
E	O	O	W	P	S	N	O	M	E	D	A	R	K	E
K	W	D	F	R	E	E	L	Y	D	L	I	H	C	L

◇ **Bonus Trivia**

What verse of a psalm about zeal was quoted with reference to Christ?

127

Hope

ABOUND	MY
ALL	NOT ASHAMED
ASSURANCE	ONE
BLESSED	PARTAKER
CALLING	PATIENCE
COME	PLOW
CONTINUALLY	POOR
DEATH	PROMISE
DOOR	REASON
FATHERS	RECEIVE
GLORY	REJOICE
GOD	RIGHTEOUSNESS
GOSPEL	SAVED
ISRAEL	SECURE
LIFE	SET
LIVELY	STEDFAST
LORD	TREE
MAN	TRUTH
MERCY	WORD

```
M P R O O P F E A C E C O M E
L E J O Y A A R O O D A P Y L
E C R C A R T S M E R L Y L S
A N S C N T H E R A O L A S J
R E G A Y A E T S W L I E O D
S I O N V K R D O A Y N C S D
I T S H W E S R U A S G N H E
S A P T A R D N D U L L A U M
T P E U M E I E O E P Y R G A
E L L R A T S E S V R D U L H
D I D T N S T F E I O N S O S
F V H O E H R I C E M U S R A
A E C L G G E L U C I O A Y T
S L B I I N E A R E S B E N O
T Y R E J O I C E R E A S O N
```

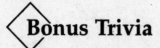

Bonus Trivia

What verse in Hosea contrasts mercy and sacrifice?

"I desired mercy, and not sacrifice; and the knowledge of God more than burnt offerings." (Hosea 6:6)

128

Gifts

ADMINISTRATION	INTERPRETATION
BODY	KNOWLEDGE
CHARITY	LEAD
COMMUNICATION	LIFE
COUNSELING	MERCY
CRAFTSMANSHIP	MIRACLES
DISCERNMENT	ONE
EDIFY	PROMISE
ENCOURAGEMENT	PROPHESY
FAITH	SHEPHERD
GIVING	SPIRIT
HEALING	TEACHING
HELP	TONGUES
INDESCRIBABLE	WISDOM

```
S T I R I P S H E P H E R D P
P R O M I S E T E G I V I N G
C C O M M U N I C A T I O N A
C R A F T S M A N S H I P E C
A L I F E D I F Y R T M E G T
A D M I N I S T R A T I O N N
N G N I H C A E T P S T A I E
M O D S I W H E A L I N G L M
E L B A B I R C S E D N I E N
D N L E Y P R O P H E S Y S R
A W M I R A C L E S M A D N E
E G D E L W O N K L E L O U C
L Y T O N G U E S G R E B O S
T N E M E G A R U O C N E C I
I I N A C H A R I T Y O J O D
```

◇ **Bonus Trivia**

What is the verse about God's love and his chastening?

"Whom the Lord loveth he chasteneth, and scourgeth every son whom he receiveth." (Hebrews 12:6)

129

Names of Jesus Christ

ALPHA AND THE OMEGA (3)

BELOVED SON

BRANCH

BREAD OF LIFE (3)

CORNERSTONE

COUNSELOR

EMMANUEL

EVERLASTING FATHER (2)

FRIEND

HIGH PRIEST (2)

LAMB OF GOD (2)

LIGHT OF THE WORLD

MORNING STAR (2)

PRINCE OF PEACE

PROPITIATION

RABBI

ROOT

SAVIOUR

SON OF DAVID

SON OF GOD (3)

SON OF MAN (3)

THE LIFE (2)

THE TRUTH (2)

THE VINE (2)

THE WAY (2)

TRUE LIGHT

WONDERFUL

Number in parentheses is how many words may be found separately within the puzzle. (Ex. "Lamb" is found in one place and "of God" is found in another, while "Son" and "of" and "God" are all found in different places, and "Son of David" is all together.)

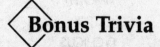

```
C O U N S E L O R A G E M O Y
O S I G N I T S A L R E V E A
R O F R O R N B S T A U A J W
N N A M U D O E H T B F N O O
E E H T E F I L M S B R D T N
R M H I G H T O A M I I T H D
S O N O F D A V I D A E H G E
T R A T S D I E P V I N E I R
O N L O A O T D F R D D U L F
N I P B U G I S T A I A O E U
E N H R L F P O O T E E U L
E G A A Y O O N H N H H S R U
F C M N C R R E F O S E E T B
I B E C A E P F O E C N I R P
L I G H T O F T H E W O R L D
```

◇ Bonus Trivia

What is the great saying about Enoch?

"Enoch walked with God: and he was not;
for God took him." (Genesis 5:24)

130
Men of the New Testament

ANANIAS	JUDE
ANDREW	LUKE
APOLLOS	MARK
AQUILA	MATTHEW
BARNABAS	ONESIMUS
BARTHOLOMEW	PAUL
CORNELIUS	PETER
DEMAS	PHILEMON
EUTYCHUS	PHILIP
FELIX	SILAS
FESTUS	SIMON
HEROD	STEPHEN
JAMES	THOMAS
JOHN	TIMOTHY
JOSEPH	TITUS
JUDAS	TYCHICUS

```
M A T T H E W E R D N A H E N
R T A S I X E F E L I X W T E
F H Y H T O M I T H O N O J H
O E N I M N O N E S I M U S P
T Y S P H I L I P A U D A E E
S H U T R X O P Y D E B H M T
A A I J U D H J P K A P P A S
M N L Y A S T U U N A M E J E
E O E I R A R L R D E U S O U
D M N Y S T A A M S A M O H T
H E R O D S B Q N M I S J N Y
R L O S T I T U S H A M A P C
E I C T Y C H I C U S R O I H
F H O R P A U L E S O B K N U
A P O L L O S A I N A N A E S
```

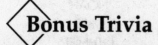

Bonus Trivia

Who said, "Woe unto him that striveth with his Maker!"

The Lord (Isaiah 45:9)

131
Men of the Old Testament

AARON
ABEL
ABRAHAM
ADAM
AHAZ
ASA
ASHER
BENJAMIN
CAIN
CALEB
DANIEL
DAVID
EHUD
ELI
ELIAS
ELIJAH
ELISHA
ENOCH
ESAU
EZEKIEL
HAGGAI
HAMAN
HEZEKIAH
HOSEA

ISAAC
ISAIAH
ISHMAEL
JACOB
JOASH
JOEL
JONAH
JONATHAN
JOSHUA
LOT
MANASSEH
METHUSELAH
MOSES
NAAMAN
NEHEMIAH
NOAH
OBED
OTHNIEL
REHOBOAM
SAMUEL
SAUL
SETH
SOLOMON

B	E	L	A	C	A	I	N	A	A	M	A	N	E	R
E	Z	E	L	I	A	S	D	A	N	I	E	L	L	E
N	E	I	E	R	Q	H	E	V	L	H	I	O	I	H
J	K	N	Z	S	A	M	U	E	L	S	S	T	J	O
A	I	H	A	G	G	A	I	P	H	A	E	Y	A	B
M	E	T	H	U	S	E	L	A	H	O	T	S	H	O
I	L	O	V	E	P	L	A	B	A	J	H	W	D	A
N	K	B	L	N	E	Q	J	E	H	O	A	J	I	M
A	M	E	N	O	M	O	L	O	S	N	S	M	V	A
M	B	D	J	R	N	D	S	E	S	A	A	H	A	N
A	P	H	S	A	S	G	A	E	W	H	M	A	D	A
H	Y	C	T	A	C	I	S	A	A	C	U	I	U	S
A	S	H	E	R	U	O	P	R	H	O	G	A	H	S
O	A	K	V	Q	M	L	B	C	A	N	Z	S	E	E
N	E	H	E	M	I	A	H	E	Z	E	K	I	A	H

◇ Bonus Trivia

Finish the proverb that says of wisdom,
"Length of days is in her right hand—"

"and in her left hand riches and honor."
(Proverbs 3:16)

132

Who Is Jesus?

ADVOCATE

BROTHER

CAPTAIN

CHRIST

COUNSELOR

DELIVERER

DOOR

FRIEND

HEAD

HOLY

JUDGE

KING

LAMB

LIFE

LIGHT

LOVE

MASTER

MEDIATOR

MESSIAH

PEACE

PHYSICIAN

PRIEST

PROPHET

RABBI

RANSOM

REDEEMER

REVELATION

RIGHTEOUS

ROCK

RULER

SAVIOUR

SHEPHERD

SON

TEACHER

TRUTH

VINE

WAY

WISDOM

WORD OF GOD

```
H S A D V O C A T E A C H E R
E U N A N L L E G S T S C N B
A O O T U E H N R R E R T I R
D E S S H P I O F E V I U V O
O T H I O K C R F T O B R T T
G H E R L K I C F S L M C P H
F G P H Y S I C I A N A A E E
O I H C W I S D O M J L I A R
D R E R A N S O M E N U T C E
R L R O T A I D E M L R D E M
O O D M E S S I A H R I O G E
W L I G H T I B B A R E F O E
S A V I O U R E R E V I L E D
R D Y N O I T A L E V E R U E
N I A T P A C O U N S E L O R
```

◇ Bonus Trivia

Who asked Christ the question, "Good
Master, what shall I do that I may inherit
eternal life?"

The rich young ruler (Mark 10:17)

133

Old Testament Heroes

AARON	JEPHTHAH
ABEL	JEREMIAH
ABRAHAM	JOB
BARAK	JONAH
CALEB	JONATHAN
CHOSEN	JOSEPH
DANIEL	JOSHUA
DAVID	MALACHI
DEBORAH	MICAH
ELDERS	MOSES
ELIJAH	NAOMI
ELISHA	NEHEMIAH
ENOCH	NOAH
ESTHER	POWER
EZEKIEL	PROPHETS
EZRA	RAHAB
FAITH	RULERS
GIDEON	RUTH
ISAAC	SAMSON
ISAIAH	SAMUEL
JACOB	SARAH

```
A R E H T S E P R O P H E T S
O B A R A K H A R O B E D I A
L A R U I M O A N O S M A S M
E H U A R A E X E E A N P A U
I A T M H A O N S J P A O I E
K R H S N A L O O O E H W A L
E S I N E B M B H S A T E H S
Z L C O H E N O C H S A R A H
E M S R E L U R H U R N B J A
N A C A M D H T I A F O E I H
O L H A I E A R Z E B J L L T
E A A O A R N V I S T O A E H
D C N V H S D M I C A H C I P
I H O L L E I N A D A N S A E
G I J E R E M I A H P E S O J
```

Bonus Trivia

Complete Paul's sentence, "Where the spirit of the Lord is,—"

"there is liberty." (2 Corinthians 3:17)

134

More on Creation

BEAST	LIGHT
BEGINNING	MAN
BLESS	MIST
BONE	MOON
BREATHE	MORNING
CATTLE	NIGHT
CREATED	PLANT
CREATURES	REST
DARKNESS	RIB
DAY	RULE
DIVIDE	SAID
DUST	SEAS
EARTH	SEASON
EVENING	SEED
FISH	SEVEN
FORM	SIGNS
FOWL	SIX
FRUIT	STAR
GOD	SUN
GOOD	TREE
GRASS	VOID
HEAVEN	WATER
HERB	WHALES
IMAGE	WOMAN
LAND	WORK
LIFE	YEARS

```
R R E S T E F I L D A Y X I S
E V E N I N G O D A O B O N E
T G V O I D O B I R D O I D R
A R S S E L B E E K S N G U U
W W E A S U N G D N B E A S T
H O O E G A M I I E R V R T A
A S M S E E D N V S E E T A E
L B I A H S D N I S A S H R R
E Y R F N I I I D E T A E R C
S N O E F G A N D A H E A L Y
F O W L H N S G N L E S V I E
R O O T L S S C A T T L E G A
U M R U L E A V L P M S N H R
I R K M E A R T H A A I I T S
T N A L P S G G N I N R O M E
```

Bonus Trivia

What book tells about "the song of Moses...
and the Lamb"?

Revelation (15:3)

135

Jonah

AMITTAI	NINEVEH
ANGRY	PRAY
ANIMALS	REPENT
ASHES	SACKCLOTH
BELLY	SACRIFICE
BUSH	SAILORS
CAPTAIN	SEA
CARGO	SHEOL
DEEP	SHIP
DELIVERANCE	STORM
FISH	SUN
FORTY	SWALLOW
HEBREW	TARSHISH
KING	VOWS
LOTS	WAVES
MERCY	WIND

```
S A C R I F I C E C F T X W B
A S T A K D C A P T A I N U E
I H R E P E N T M R O T S C L
L E B S U N I N E V E H H H L
O S W A L L O W B E E F I E Y
R A I R R S O R Y B C B P S C
S C N S O A N G R Y W Q X I R
Y K D E L I V E R A N C E P E
A C L E T F W K A X R J F U M
R L C O E R A N I M A L S N F
P O A L E P V J P N I E F Y L
Y T R O F H E E B I G T Y Y W
H H G T A R S H I S H U T J X
O X O S W O V N J X Y D O A Q
H B L C W B L N U T B L S B I
```

◇ Bonus Trivia

What is the rest of the prayer of David
beginning, "O Lord, open thou my lips—"?

"and my mouth shall shew forth thy praise."
(Psalm 51:15)

136

Judges, Prophets, & Leaders

AARON	JOHN
AMOS	JONAH
DANIEL	JOSHUA
DEBORAH	MALACHI
ELI	MICAH
ELIJAH	MOSES
ELISHA	NAHUM
EZEKIEL	NATHAN
EZRA	NEHEMIAH
GIDEON	OBADIAH
HABAKKUK	SAMSON
HAGGAI	SAMUEL
HOSEA	SAUL
ISAIAH	ZECHARIAH
JEREMIAH	ZEPHANIAH

```
G I D E O N O K U E E X K B P
R S F H A B A K K U K Q F Y M
N A T H A N A J E R E M I A H
E I S E R M O D O D J M R D N
H A E S O H O E I S A M S O N
E H D S N O D S V A H N B C T
M Z E P H A N I A H H U I D O
I S R Z E C H A R I A H A E D
A K P A E B B S A M U E L B L
H V V Q K K F R A V I I U O J
M R V W D P I L Y U D C N R P
P E L I S H A E Z G L Y A A N
F W O Q Q C N E L I J A H H D
J O N A H A G G A I M N U Y V
V F U I V G Y T O M J O M D G
```

◇ **Bonus Trivia**

Whose song begins, "Sing ye to the Lord, for he hath triumphed gloriously"?

Miriam's, after the crossing of the Red Sea (Exodus 15:21)

137
In the Beginning

ADAM

ANIMALS

BIRDS

CREATURES

CURSED

DARKNESS

DOMINION

EARTH

EDEN

EVE

EVENING

EVIL

FIRMAMENT

GARDEN

GENERATIONS

GOOD

GROUND

HEAVENS

KNOWLEDGE

LIGHT

MORNING

PLANTS

RIB

SERPENT

SEVENTH

SWARM

TREE

VEGETATION

WATER

```
C R E A T U R E S L I G H T E
O F I R M A M E N T A Q O D V
S H E B J V M J I R Q C E O E
S E R P E N T A D P V N A M D
E A K N O W L E D G E N R I A
V V J I J A N I M A L S T N R
E E J X W T K E X Q X O H I K
N N G E N E R A T I O N S O N
T S X E G R G E R A X D Q N E
H O E G T N E V C U R S E D S
D P Q B R A I E V I L Q U B S
E K L B V O T N B O O W Q W N
Y D G E U L U I R S T N A L P
T J H C X W W N O O C R W M F
D X D C J V R G D N M S T D S
```

Bonus Trivia

Who received the promise that, if he meditated on God's law, "Then thou shalt make thy way prosperous, and then thou shalt have good success"?

Joshua (Joshua 1:8)

138
More on the Flood

ALTAR	FORTY
ANIMALS	HAM
ARARAT	JAPHETH
ARK	MALE
BIRDS	MOUNTAINS
CLOUDS	NOAH
COMMANDED	PITCH
COVENANT	RAIN
CUBITS	RAINBOW
CYPRESS	RAVEN
DECKS	SEVEN
DOVE	SHEM
EARTH	WATERS
FEMALE	WIND

```
R A I N B O W E V O D S S M J
C M O U N T A I N S D F E S A
S A F S A X D D S H E D C R P
H L L D D E K T C L G V A J H
E E D U H N I T V R F R E A E
M A J O V B I R D S A C M N T
A R K L U P D W A T E R S I H
L T N C O M M A N D E D X M G
T H N Y O D C E V B T G L A T
A M R P N V T V R F E M A L E
R U I R S H E M E C O S I S O
A M D E C K S N X P H R B L M
V H V S A R S E A F E M T S F
E E C S T N U J Y N F N L Y K
N N I A R C N T P G T W I K T
```

◇ **Bonus Trivia**

Who expressed the wish, "Oh that my head were waters, and mine eyes a fountain of tears!"

Jeremiah, "the weeping prophet" (Jeremiah 9:1)

139

Ruth & Esther

AHASUERUS	MORDECAI
BANQUET	NAOMI
BARLEY	PALACE
BETHLEHEM	PERSIA
BOAZ	POOR
DAVID	QUEEN
ELIMELECH	REAPERS
GALLOWS	REDEEM
HAMAN	SCEPTER
HARVEST	THRESHING
HUSBAND	VASHTI
MOAB	WIDOW

```
D T I J N E R E D E E M J M T
R S M A D P A L B R O O P O Q
V N M D F Y O S R E P A E R O
T A H A S U E R U S L B R D V
H A R V E S T H D A N I S E S
R U H I A U H V C L G P I C G
E C S D E S C E P T E R A A U
S L C B E T H L E H E M L I N
H M I F A A O T B A R L E Y D
I C D M G N E C I A O B X N S
N P Y X E F D I R W N A O M I
G N M J G L B O S I N Q W A E
K S G G Y Y E D F D O C U K Z
Q K F I H M E C V O Q U E E N
N Q K K K U U U H W R R C N T
```

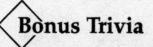

Bonus Trivia

What prophet cried, "Woe unto him that
giveth his neighbor drink"?

Habakkuk (Habakkuk 2:15)

140

Moses

AARON
BASKET
BRICKS
CHARIOTS
COMMANDMENTS
CURTAIN
EGYPTIANS
HEBREWS
HORSES
LAMB
LOCUSTS
NILE
PASSOVER

PHARAOH
PILLAR
PLAGUES
PRIESTHOOD
SABBATH
SACRIFICE
SINAI
SMOKE
STAFF
SWARMS
TABERNACLE
WILDERNESS

```
S T A F F S W A R M S L I G B
A A R O N I L E K O B I O T G
C B B J N N Y O O A X M B W W
R E P B U A N I C U R T A I N
I R Y V A I F W N U U R M L S
F N K R O T R H O R S E S D I
I A V Q C C H A R I O T S E P
C C O M M A N D M E N T S R U
E L H J B R I C K S G E H N S
R E E M R Q B O K J L K M E E
A T B N L I M F T E Y S F S U
L P R I E S T H O O D A J S G
L H E G Y P T I A N S B L L A
I M W G M V H G Q H N F C B L
P A S S O V E R H O A R A H P
```

◇ **Bonus Trivia**

Finish the beatitude, "Blessed are the poor in spirit;—"

"For theirs is the kingdom of heaven."
(Matthew 5:3)

141

Daniel

ABEDNEGO

BABYLON

BELSHAZZAR

BRONZE

CHALDEANS

DARIUS

DREAM

EXILES

FURNACE

GOLD

HORN

IRON

KINGDOM

LIONS

MAGICIANS

MESHACH

NEBUCHADNEZZAR

PERSIANS

PROPHECY

SHADRACH

VISIONS

WRITING

```
I E S H A C H M T B N B R F
V A Q X L S Y S H A D R A C H
E G E K I N G D O M W N B H N
K I T G O L D A R I U S Y A N
Y C W R N I E F N E B S L L Q
U I I U S Q H S U F A S O D O
S A N U M S J Y K G O M N E H
N N E B U C H A D N E Z Z A R
S S U X B X V T F H I N H N J
P W R I T I N G F U O M Q S R
V J Y W S O D Y N R R H Q Y E
P D I I P U D A B E D N E G O
S T O T B E L S H A Z Z A R K
S N A I S R E P R O P H E C Y
S P X Z R E K H X J E G N G E
```

Bonus Trivia

What is Paul's saying about "the yoke of bondage"?

"Stand fast therefore in the liberty wherewith
Christ hath made us free, and be not
entangled again with the yoke of bondage."
(Galatians 5:1)

142

Kings

AHAZ	JOSIAH
AHAZIAH	MANASSEH
AMAZIAH	MENAHEM
AZARIAH	OMRI
DAVID	PEKAH
HEZEKIAH	REHOBOAM
HOSHEA	SAUL
JEHOASH	SHALLUM
JEHU	SOLOMON
JEROBOAM	UZZIAH
JOASH	ZECHARIAH
JORAM	

```
S H A L L U M A N A S S E H B
J E R O B O A M M N G O D K M
O E M P K T P A M E N A H E M
S R H Y Q B Z E B A X M P E H
I E O O X I P A K K R R D H N
A H A Z A R I A H A A O O O J
H O E H J S D Q Y U H E J S E
A B D Z E C H A R I A H O H X
Z O V V E K C N F D T L A E G
I A K C P K O Y V C O Z S A E
A M C H H G I G T M G I H D L
H F V C S T I A O S I F A I V
D W Y F R O J N H A W E V V K
F C R L Y P V Z F U Z Z I A H
H Z J D A R V J H L T V S D P
```

143

Pentecost

APOSTLES	MEDES
BREAD	PENTECOST
CONVERTS	PETER
DARKNESS	PRAYER
FIRE	PROPHESY
GALILEANS	PROPHET
GLAD	SIGNS
HEAVEN	SPIRIT
JERUSALEM	TEACHING
JOEL	TONGUES
JOHN	WIND
JUDEA	WITNESSES

```
P E N T E C O S T C M O A Q X
R X J E R U S A L E M F L O H
O P C A L H P U X U C Z X P Q
P U H C I W I T N E S S E S F
H B Y H D A R K N E S S E D H
E Q G I U U I T G B T A E M T
S R V N W P T E H P O R P K O
Y D E G A L I L E A N S R R N
Q N H T M T U A K J N U A Q G
F I R E E F U S P J G U Y L U
P W D M A P O S T L E S E B E
A E D U J V N C O N V E R T S
S G T T O O E U J R G E Q F K
W T Y E H L E N L W A L S Z R
H S I G N S G L A D Z X X U Y
```

Bonus Trivia

Of whose pursuit of the enemy is the phrase used, "Faint, yet pursuing"?

144

Easter

ANGEL	PRIEST
ARIMATHEA	RESURRECTION
COUNCIL	RISEN
EARTHQUAKE	ROBE
EMMAUS	ROOM
GALILEE	SABBATH
JERUSALEM	SEPULCHRE
JOHN	SKULL
MAGDALENE	STONE
MARY	SUNRISE
MOUNTAIN	TEMPLE
PETER	THOMAS
PILATE	

```
U P R I E S T V S A M O H T A
V I E M M A U S U N R I S E N
Y L U T A R I M A T H E A M G
R A F L E R O B E B B D M P E
C T X N P R Y O B M B W R L L
J E R U S A L E M R D A J E L
O A E L E I G U W H F K T P U
H R E S U R R E C T I O N H K
N T N N W I E R H C L U P E S
L H T H F U X G A L I L E E T
I Q S P C P R L G B C X M H O
R U S Y L U Z M O U N T A I N
M A G D A L E N E O U S B J E
R K X X P G M U M J O B P P P
X E J N L V O K T E C W P V F
```

◇ **Bonus Trivia**

What verse of a psalm speaks of God's pity for his children?

"Like as a father pitieth his children, so the Lord pitieth them that fear him." (Psalm 103:13)

145

Sermon on the Mount

BLESSED

DISCIPLES

DOOR

ENEMIES

EYE

FIGS

FOOL

FORGIVE

GLORY

GRAPES

HUNGER

KINGDOM

KNOCK

LAMP

LIGHT

LOVE

MEEK

MERCIFUL

MOURN

PEACEMAKERS

PERSECUTED

PRAYER

PROPHETS

REJOICE

REWARD

SALT

THIRST

TOOTH

```
Q R E Y A R P N N R E W A R D
G C E F I G S R H U N G E R A
P Y D O O R U K O V W J P Y X
E Y I R T O O T H P O S M R M
R E S G M Z L R T I H Z A O B
S V C I C K N O C K B E L L X
E O I V L M E E K V F F T G T
C L P E A C E M A K E R S S H
U I L J R N G R A P E S D V T
T G E O E M A D C F S E C H X
E H S M I L U M K I N G D O M
D T I J L X I Q Q E F E W W U
J E E R S S R G O G L U H W J
S X D E S S E L B L U H L T E
A X A L G T C Z J G M Y W R L
```

◇ Bonus Trivia

In what parable is the expression, "Take thine ease, eat, drink, and be merry"?

In the parable of the foolish rich man
(Luke 12:19)

293

146

Israelites in the Wilderness

AARON

AMALEKITES

BALAAM

BRONZE

CALF

CAMP

COMMANDMENTS

FIRE

FORTY

GLORY

GOLD

ISRAELITES

JETHRO

JORDAN

KORAH

MANNA

MOSES

MOUNTAIN

OFFERING

PRIESTS

QUAIL

SINAI

SNAKES

TABERNACLE

TABLETS

```
B T A B L E T S S Y S V F H U
R A M A L E K I T E S N Q S M
O B L P R I E S T S W Q O O B
N E G A W O R O Y Q A R T I L
Z R W X A N N V D K U D K N D
E N K M Y M E P H S N A K E S
S A L X Q E Z O F F E R I N G
E C O M M A N D M E N T S L O
S L C B R O O R H T E J O I L
O E Y K H Q Q Q D K O R A H D
M O U N T A I N V R Y B M N E
C A L F O R T Y D U F L H H W
Q A N K I S R A E L I T E S X
B E M N X R N I A N I S A X G
Y O R P A B E J H D E W E I D
```

◇ **Bonus Trivia**

Finish Paul's saying, "In Jesus Christ neither circumcision availeth any thing, nor uncircumcision; but—"

"faith which worketh by love." (Galatians 5:6)

147

Foes of Israel

AMALEKITES

AMMONITES

AMORITES

ASSYRIANS

BABYLONIANS

CAANANITES

EDOMITES

EGYPTIANS

GREEKS

HITTITES

JEBUSITES

MEDES

MOABITES

PERIZZITES

PHILISTINES

ROMANS

SIDONIANS

```
Z M P A P H I L I S T I N E S
D A M M O N I T E S N M N P A
C A A N A N I T E S R A H E S
Y M S W I S E Z T D E J M I S
Q A K Q H N K J L I E H D O Y
J L I O T Q X F B M T O U R R
P E R I Z Z I T E S N E H W I
L K B A B Y L O N I A N S J A
U I Y U K Z M O A B I T E S N
Q T V S S E H N M H W N T V S
Y E L K D I S X M B S X I K O
O S O E F E T C K V G D M R W
J B S E D B W E X K R U O T I
A M O R I T E S S Z Y C D A C
L V E G Y P T I A N S N E K C
```

Bonus Trivia

Complete the saying in Job, "Thy that plow iniquity, and sow wickedness—"

"reap the same." (Job 4:8)

148

Jacob & Sons

ASHER

BENJAMIN

CANAAN

COAT

DONKEY

EGYPT

EPHRAIM

FAMINE

FLOCKS

GAD

GOSHEN

GRAIN

ISRAEL

JOSEPH

JUDAH

LADDER

MARRIAGE

PHARAOH

REBEKAH

REUBEN

SLAVE

STARS

WELL

WRESTLE

ZEBULUN

```
I U S G R A I N I K S R Q E K
H P E S O J U D A H S M D P N
F M H E K S K V O E K P W N M
L A D D E R H H M N B F L H D
O R N R E U B E N C K R C M Y
C R C C A N A A N W H E F U Z
K I E Y S F X T I R T P Y G E
S A F B E N J A M I N H M P B
L G D A E N C O B M M A H I U
A E K J H K Z C F R F R M F L
V S T A R S A M I H A A U B U
E R H Z L B I H N I M O G Q N
G A D E K M U A M R I H A L M
F T X R R H S X B H N W J K I
I S R A E L L E W R E S T L E
```

◇ Bonus Trivia

What prophet commanded, "Make you a new heart and a new spirit; for why will ye die"?

Ezekiel (Ezekiel 18:31)

149

Revelation

AMEN	JOHN
ANGEL	JUDGMENT
APOSTLES	LAMB
BABYLON	NATIONS
BEAST	PLAGUE
BOOKS	SAINTS
BOWLS	SCROLL
CHURCHES	SEVEN
CRYSTAL	SPIRIT
DEAD	THOUSAND
EARTH	THRONE
HEAVEN	TRUMPETS
HORNS	TWELVE
JERUSALEM	

```
G L Y O D F C R Y S T A L V R
C T R U M P E T S C M S D K O
H H H E A V E N R R N L A M B
U O O R P N A T I O N S X E A
R U R Y O V G H D L V Y W Q B
C S N K V N O E W L E L M D Y
H A S U W L E T L O T Q Y Q L
E N P J E R U S A L E M U W O
S D I O U H V W S T D Q A S N
N A R H S D E F G T W E L V E
E T I N M T G P D A H W A A U
V A T N T Q L M U M O O W D G
E M R N T K Z E E B O O K S A
S E N T Z S W D S N T X R G L
U N L E H Z J T M I T S Y G P
```

◇ **Bonus Trivia**

What is Christ's saying about climbing up "some other way" into the sheepfold?

"He that entereth not by the door into the sheepfold, but climbeth up some other way, the same is a thief and a robber." (John 10:1)

150

Nativity

ANGEL	JOSEPH
AUGUSTUS	JOY
BETHLEHEM	JUDEA
CHILD	MANGER
DECREE	MARY
DREAM	MESSIAH
EGYPT	NIGHT
FIRSTBORN	PEACE
GLORY	SAVIOR
HEROD	SHEPHERDS
HOUSE	STAR
INN	VIRGIN
JERUSALEM	

```
R Z S X T R L P E D P E A C E
A U G U S T U S I P I N N H Q
T K L F O D T K O I S A G I E
S A V I O R E P Q C E Q E L V
H R U R A L S C Y D O J L D A
E T M S X I U Y U G X Q G E D
P R X T B Y O J O S E P H C Z
H O D B E T H L E H E M A R Y
E I A O H W J E R U S A L E M
R O Z R M B V I R G I N W E Y
D E O N W I C W Y O I G I M T
S H R M L V N T M G D E H A T
N X M E S S I A H I V R W E H
F Q N Q K F L T C S G L O R Y
V F B K F E J W R I H H I D B
```

Bonus Trivia

What is the proverb about wisdom being "the principal thing"?

"Wisdom is the principal thing; therefore get wisdom: and with all thy getting get understanding." (Proverbs 4:7)

151

Israelite Priests

AARON	JUDGE
AHIMAAZ	KINGS
AHITUB	LAW
AMARIAH	LEADER
AZARIAH	LEVITICUS
CHRONICLES	MESSAGE
ELEAZAR	NUMBERS
EXODUS	PHINEHAS
EZRA	SAMUEL
FAITHFUL	SERAIAH
GOD	TABERNACLE
HIGH	TEMPLE
HILKIAH	WORSHIPER
INSTRUCTIONS	ZADOK

```
Z A I A E L C A N R E B A T L
A H N H H A S E R A I A H G N
D I S T I Z F A I T H M P O O
O T T M L A T E M P L O L D R
K U R A K R L A W S I K U S A
O B U A I I G E F R S J F E A
S U C Z A A H H R E A U H L S
U Q T C H H G A X B M D T C A
C Z I T T I Z O S M U G I I H
I A O I H A D G A U E E A N E
T A N O E U N R O N L A F O N
I M S L S I Z L E A D E R R I
V I E W K E T E M P L E A H H
E H W O R S H I P E R C B C P
L A M A R I A H M E S S A G E
```

Bonus Trivia

What is the rest of the proverb, "My son, if sinners entice thee—"?

"Consent thou not" (Proverbs 1:10)

305

152
Mothers in the Bible

AHINOAM

ATHALIAH

AZUBAH

BATHSHEBA

BILHAH

EUNICE

EVE

HAGGITH

HANNAH

HEPHZIBAH

HERODIAS

JEDIDAH

JEHOADDAN

JERUSHA

JOCHEBED

LEAH

MAACAH

MARY

MESHULLEMETH

NAOMI

RACHEL

RAHAB

REBEKAH

RUTH

SALOME

SARAH

TAMAR

VASHTI

ZEBUDAH

ZILPAH

```
I B A H A R Z E B U D A H S H
T S H L Z T J E R U S H A Z J
H A K M U L I M O A N L B A E
S T H O B I A H I N O A M L H
A H E T A J E D I D A H N E O
V A P M H Z O R A C H E L A A
S L H J E R S O B I L H A H D
N I Z A E L A V E V E V T H D
H A I H H M L E H A N N A H A
A H B I A A O U S N J R M T N
K M A N G A M N H S A U A O Y
E T H O G C E I T S J T R R A
B K H A I A H C A V E H A K M
E I A M T H L E B K T M O S I
R J O C H E B E D Z I L P A H
```

◇ Bonus Trivia

Whose is the saying about the axe laid to the root of the trees?

John the Baptist's (Matthew 3:10)

153

Praise in Psalms

ADMIRATION	JUST
APPRECIATION	KINGDOM
BLESSINGS	LIGHT
CELEBRATE	LOVE
CREATION	LOVING
DAVID	MAJESTY
DELIVERER	MUSIC
EXALT	PATIENT
FAITHFUL	PRAISE
FORGIVENESS	PRAYERS
GLORIOUS	ROCK
GLORY	SHARED
HEARTFELT	SING
HOPE	THANKS
JOY	WORKS

```
W F L F O R G I V E N E S S L
O A M A J E S T Y H K A C G O
R I A G L O R I O U S T R N T
K T Q P L O V I N G I M E I H
S H R S P E X A L T N U A S A
N F U T C R D L H W G S S S N
O U P P V E E A I O X I I E K
I L A R L K L C V G P C O L S
T G T A A O I E I I H E N B T
A L I I J Y V N B A D T Y J D
R O E S U B E E G R T Z A O E
I R N E S O R R N D A I B Y R
M Y T N T N E I S E O T O T A
D B S T A E R C O P S M E N H
A R O C K H E A R T F E L T S
```

154

Israelite Feasts in Leviticus

ATONEMENT

COMMITMENT

CROPS

DELIVERANCE

DESERT

EGYPT

EXODUS

FELLOWSHIP

FIRSTFRUITS

GOD

GUIDANCE

JOY

LEVITICUS

LORD

PASSOVER

PROTECTION

PROTECTION

RESTORATION

SEVEN

SLAVERY

TABERNACLES

THANKSGIVING

TRUMPETS

TRUST

UNLEAVENED BREAD

WEEKS

```
T P G N I V I G S K N A H T D
R R L G U I D A N C E L T A W
U O E N E W E E K S U S E M O
M T V E G G S J O Y E R T P I
P E I V Y O E I U L B P N F N
T O T E P D R S C D T S O I O
N T I S T L T A E N P T I R I
E A C E U E N N E O W I T S T
M G U V P R E M R M L O C T A
E M S M E V T C L O R D E F R
N M U B A I E X O D U S T R O
O R A E M S L A V E R Y O U T
T T L M R E V O S S A P R I S
A N O F E L L O W S H I P T E
U C D E L I V E R A N C E S R
```

◇ **Bonus Trivia**

What did Paul call "the first commandment with promise"?

"Honour thy father and mother." (Ephesians 6:2)

155
Queens and Kings

ABIGAIL	JEHU
ABIJAH	JEROBOAM
AHAZIAH	JEZEBEL
AHINOAM	JORAM
ATHALIAH	MAACHAH
BAASHA	MICHAL
BATHSHEBA	NADAB
BELSHAZZAR	NEBUCHADNEZZAR
CANDACE	QUEEN OF SHEBA
CYRUS	REHOBOAM
DAVID	SOLOMON
ELAH	TAHPENES
ESTHER	VASHTI
JEHOSHAPHAT	XERXES

```
A M J E H O S H A P H A T T R
B A T H S H E B A X E R X A E
I A H A I L A H T A H A Z H H
J C K B C Y R U S N T Z A P O
A H J A M I C H A L E Z H E B
H A O A T J T L P N C A I N O
J H R S Z S E M D O A H N E A
D O A H E B A A H M D S O S M
A U M A E O H A E O N L A Z I
V H N Z B C I S E L A E M B T
I E E O U Z E Q H O C B E A H
D J R B A X U L T S H O L D S
T E E H R A B I G A I L A A A
J N A E S T H E R K T P H N V
Q U X A B E H S F O N E E U Q
```

Bonus Trivia

Who asked God to put his tears into His bottle?

David (Psalm 56:8)

156

Fathers

AARON

ABRAHAM

ADAM

AHAB

ALPHAEUS

BENJAMIN

DAN

DAVID

ELI

ELKANAH

ENOCH

GAD

HAM

ISAAC

JACOB

JAPHETH

JEPHTHAH

JETHRO

JOB

JONATHAN

JOSEPH

JUDAH

KISH

LABAN

LEVI

MORDECAI

MOSES

NAPHTALI

NOAH

REUBEN

SAMUEL

SAUL

SETH

SHEM

SOLOMON

```
T K O J E P H T H A H L E V I
J B M E L K A N A H N D A N L
A S A O I S A A C O T B B I J
P L E L R J D I V A D E R L O
H O U O P D K N O A H N A A S
E L T A R H E I J O B J H T E
T A J E S H A C S K E A A H P
H B O C S T E A H L M M P H
L A N N A O E E U I I A A C
B N A E M L M T J S M N M N O
O A T B U O A P H J E N O C H
C A H U E M H N O U H L S H T
A R A E L O A O I D S I E A G
J O N R J N B T C A B C S M A
K N J O N A T H A H A D A M D
```

315

157

Animals & Birds of the Bible

ADDER	HARE
ANT	HART
ANTELOPE	HAWK
APE	HEIFER
ASP	HORNET
ASS	HORSE
BADGER	KID
BAT	KINE
BEAR	LAMB
BEE	LICE
BEETLE	LION
BULLOCK	LOCUST
CAMEL	MOLE
COCKATRICE	MOTH
COLT	MOUSE
DROMEDARY	OWL
EAGLE	OX
EWE	RAM
FLEA	RAVEN
FOX	SNAIL
FROG	SPARROW
GAZELLE	STORK
GNAT	SWINE
GOAT	VULTURE
GRASSHOPPER	

```
A R A E B T C A E L L E Z A G
N D D I K A N N L A Z C K H E
T H D B M B D A T U G I I O L
E A P E H E W G E B N L N R O
L W L A R R O B E W Z E E S M
O K S O L A S E B R G F V E T
P S A A T H V U L T U R E A Y
E W E M R E L E T A B O N U R
J L O B N L S S D L O G F S A
F T M I O U U N Y X O F H T D
H A W C O C K A T R I C E O E
L S K M O W J I T H F N I R M
I P E L R C L L R K R A F K O
O S P A R R O W A O G P E S R
N Z M R E P P O H S S A R G D
```

◇ Bonus Trivia

Who said of God that He is "of purer eyes than to behold evil," and that He cannot look on iniquity?

Habakkuk (Habakkuk 1:13)

317

158
Books of the
New Testament

ACTS	MARK
COLOSSIANS	MATTHEW
CORINTHIANS	PETER
EPHESIANS	PHILEMON
GALATIANS	PHILIPPIANS
HEBREWS	REVELATION
JAMES	ROMANS
JOHN	THESSALONIANS
JUDE	TIMOTHY
LUKE	TITUS

T I M O T H Y Z S M E T S O G
P H I L E M O N U S W N N B A
I Z E J K B S E T M O R A N L
Y H D S T W O L I I B K I H A
M A F S S R M G T S P M S O T
S W C A N A J A E B G W E J I
N E Z T E A L M R L Y Z H K A
A H P M S E I O A K J C P S N
I T B J V S M P N E O I E M S
S T Y E M A E L P I F M L T B
S A R A N G U N S I A W S R Y
O M F S I K W S E J L N A E P
L A J U E D U J T M O I S T J
O K S W E R B E H K W G H E B
C O R I N T H I A N S C M P U

◇ Bonus Trivia

Of whom did Christ say that they loved "the uppermost seats in the synagogues"?

The Pharisees (Luke 11:43)

319

159

Cities, Countries, and Places Paul Traveled to and Through

APPII FORUM

ARABIA

ASIA

CAESAREA

CHIOS

COOS

DAMASCUS

GREECE

ITALY

JUDEA

LYCAONIA

LYCIA

MACEDONIA

MELITA

MILETUS

NEAPOLIS

PAMPHYLIA

PAPHOS

PHILIPPI

PHOENICIA

PISIDIA

SAMOS

SELEUCIA

SMYRNA

SYRIA

THESSALONICA

THREE TAVERNS

THYATIRA

TYRE

```
N E A P O L I S B S S A A M P
C P F A G W O Z Y U O I I D I
A H N E Y H I R A T I S N A S
I O K R P S I P R E H A O M I
B E U A S A Z M P L C P A A D
A N P S I A U D S I H P C S I
R I A E T N M T N M L I Y C A
A C N A A I O O K F Y I L U I
R I R C L I D S O C F H S L
I A Y V Y A C R E V I O G P Y
T P M B S I K U N C A R R S H
A B S S L E W J E H A U E S P
Y V E U K R A T I L E M E O M
H H W M P Y S J U D E A C O A
T H R E E T A V E R N S E C P
```

◇ Bonus Trivia

What is the proverb about spreading a net in the sight of a bird?

"Surely in vain the net is spread in the sight of any bird." (Proverbs 1:17)

160

Cities, Countries, and Places Paul Traveled to and Through: Part Two

ACHAIA

AMPHIPOLIS

ANTIOCH

APOLLONIA

ASSOS

ATHENS

ATTALIA

BEREA

CENCHREA

CILICIA

CNIDUS

CORINTH

CRETE

CYPRUS

DERBE

EPHESUS

FAIR HAVENS

GALATIA

ICONIUM

JERUSALEM

LASEA

LYSTRA

MYRA

PATARA

PERGA

PHRYGIA

RHODES

ROME

SAMOTHRACIA

SIDON

SYRIA

TARSUS

TROAS

```
T Z O M E L A S U R E J M H W
A S L Y B I H A S S O S C S U
R A Y R L P S I D O N O E O F
S M S A E A R A J R I H N M S
U O T G B T O H D T J T C B N
S T R M R A M C N S S N H S E
A H A B E R E A I K Y I R A V
I R I J D A E L I L R R E I A
N A G U F S O C S S I O A T H
O C Y Z A P O E U P A C A A R
L I R L I N D S E T R N I L I
L A H H I O E R R E H I K A A
O B P U H H G O T M A D B G F
P M M R P A A E W Z N U J C M
A T H E N S C Y P R U S P L Y
```

◇ **Bonus Trivia**

To whom did God say, "The Lord searcheth all hearts"?

Solomon (1 Chronicles 28:9)

161

Tools of the Bible

ANVIL	MEASURING LINE
AWL	MILL
AX	MIRROR
BELLOWS	MORTAR
BRAZIER	NAIL
CHISEL	NEEDLE
FAN	OVEN
FILE	PEG
FURNACE	PICK
GOAD	PLANE
HAMMER	PLOW
HARROW	PLUMBLINE
HATCHET	PRESS
HOE	SAW
KNIFE	SHOVEL
LEVEL	SICKLE
MALLET	SLEDGE
MARKING TOOLS	TONGS
MATTOCK	WHEEL
MAUL	YOKE

```
A K M E A S U R I N G L I N E
Z N B G M E L D E E N M M K S
T I V K B C M P L O W I O P A
O F J I E R X N E H A R R O W
N E A O L W A R N A F R T P S
G D R E L F C Z A M I O A R E
S T V M O F K N I M L R R E N
N E J A W Y U F L E E H F S I
L L Z T S N J R S R R A L S L
E L U T I D E I N S D T E P B
E A K O C V H V F A M C V L M
H M C C K C E K O Y C H O A U
W A I K L P E G A T J E H N L
D U P L E G D E L S Z T S E P
K L B S L O O T G N I K R A M
```

Bonus Trivia

Who said, "Behold the handmaid of the Lord; be it unto me according to thy word"?

The Virgin Mary (Luke 1:38)

162

New Testament Women of the Bible

ANNA
BERNICE
CHLOE
CLAUDIA
DIANA
DORCAS
DRUSILLA
ELIZABETH
EUNICE
HERODIAS
JOANNA
JULIA
LOIS

LYDIA
MARTHA
MARY
MARY MAGDALENE
PHOEBE
PRISCILLA
RHODA
SALOME
SAPPHIRA
SUSANNA
TABITHA
TRYPHENA

```
R F A W L B A A N E H P Y R T
H E R O D I A S P E Z E M C E
E M O L A S E R C B B A A A L
S I O L A K I I E E E N H D I
F W Z C H S N R O A U N T O Z
A U R S C U N H M S D A I H A
I O K I E I P A T W O S B R B
D C L M C H L O E Z I U A C E
U L S E A R I H P P A S T G T
A Y K T Z A L L I S U R D W H
L D J R M A H M A N N A O J E
C I U A W R A T G K N Y U B T
M A N S F R U L R A S L C R Z
E N R L Y F K M I A I Z M P O
A Z E N E L A D G A M Y R A M
```

◇ Bonus Trivia

Finish Paul's saying, "The natural man
receiveth not—"?

"The things of the Spirit of God."
(1 Corinthians 2:14)

327

163
Kings from the Bible

ABIJAH
ABIMELECH
AHAB
AHAZ
AHAZIAH
AMAZIAH
AMON
ARTAXERXES
ASA
AZARIAH
DARIUS
DAVID
ELAH
HEZEKIAH
HOSEA
JEHOAHAZ

JEHOASH
JEHOIACHIN
JEHOSHAPHAT
JEHU
JEROBOAM
JOASH
JOSIAH
NADAB
OMRI
PEKAH
REHOBOAM
SAUL
SHALLUM
SOLOMON
ZECHARIAH
ZEDEKIAH
ZIMRI

```
A Z A R I A H H A I K E Z E H
H H M E J A B I J A H M N N Z
A A U Z H B Z E B A A T O A E
Z I F A N I R L K O J H M D C
I K L C M M G E B O T I A A H
A E A R S E P O A A M E S B A
H D I K U L H S H A L H S I R
Z E A H U E H P O Z A U R G I
A Z E A R C A B K L I M A Z A
H J S I M H O M L R O G E R H
A N O S S R E U A B A M C L D
O G H O E Z M D P Z O A O I U
H C H J E H O A S H I S V N F
E E S E X R E X A T R A H A Z
J E H O I A C H I N D E H K M
```

Bonus Trivia

What is the first part of the sentence which ends, "and into his courts with praise"?

"Enter into his gates with thanksgiving."
(Psalm 100:4)

164

Old Testament
Women of the Bible

ABIGAIL	JOCHEBED
ABISHAG	KETURAH
ADAH	LEAH
BATHSHEBA	MICHAL
BILHAH	MIRIAM
DEBORAH	ORPAH
DELILAH	PENINNAH
DINAH	RACHEL
ESTHER	RAHAB
EVE	REBEKAH
GOMER	RUTH
HAGAR	SARAH
HANNAH	TAMAR
HEPHZIBAH	VASHTI
HULDAH	ZERESH
JAEL	ZIPPORAH
JEZEBEL	

```
A B I G A I L E L E B E Z E J
B Z Y M G P V V R B H M L Z O
I A R O R A J E K A I B E E C
S W T E S U H F D H Z F H R H
H E M H B T T L M A N A C E E
A O T Z S Y U H P E H H A S B
G I N E F H M D K L A O R H E
S R L E A J E E I P E M F A D
A A W N R L T B R N S R K R U
R M N T I U Z O A C A P E O L
A A O L R M E R S G D H B P A
H T A A W F B A A H A E A P H
Z H H A B I Z H P E H P H I C
H A K E B E R T O B W T A Z I
P E N I N N A H Z M A I R I M
```

Bonus Trivia

Of whom was it asked in astonishment
whether he also was among the prophets?

Saul (1 Samuel 10:11-12)

165

The Lord Is My...

AVENGER	KING
CAPTAIN	LIFE
CONFIDENCE	LORD
DELIGHT	LOVING KINDNESS
DELIVERER	MAKER
ENCOURAGER	PEACE
FATHER	PRAISE
FORTRESS	PROVIDER
GLORY	REDEMPTION
GOD	ROCK
GUIDE	SALVATION
HEALER	SHEPHERD
HELP	SHIELD
HOPE	STRONG TOWER
INHERITANCE	TEACHER
JOY	VICTORY
JUDGE	

```
I H V E O P L F O R T R E S S
F R I K C D I Y R O L G S H A
E A C N I A F G U I D E C E L
S G T G H N E Y O J N O P P S
I T O H F E G P T D N L R H A
A E R K E R R H N F E O O E L
R A Y O E R G I I H V P E R V
P C C L N I K D T I E G S D A
T H A E L G E A D A D C M N T
S E O E N N T E D U N T A I I
H R D I C M R O J R O C K A O
I A V E N G E R W G O C E T N
E O D E L I V E R E R L R P I
L E N C O U R A G E R I T A N
D V S N O I T P M E D E R C S
```

◇ Bonus Trivia

Of whom did the Lord ask, "Who is this that darkeneth counsel by words without knowledge?"

Job (Job 38:2)

333

166
Birds of Palestine

BITTERN
CHICKEN
CORMORANT
CRANE
CUCKOO
DOVE
EAGLE
GIER EAGLE
GLEDE
HAWK
HEN
HERON
KITE
LAPWING
NIGHTHAWK
OSPREY

OSSIFRAGE
OSTRICH
OWL
PARTRIDGE
PEACOCK
PELICAN
PIGEON
QUAIL
RAVEN
SPARROW
STORK
SWALLOW
SWAN
TURTLEDOVE
VULTURE

```
E Y M T V F G N I W P A L N E
N P D M U T N N G V G H C I A
A E O T L R C R A H A A U G G
R A V R T W T D E W A Q C H L
C C E A U E U L K T S U K T E
I O S T R I C H E N T A L H S
K C U H E R C G A D N I S A T
G K I T E H A C A C O L B W N
L H I I R I Y D G E V H K A
E L R C F L O S E R G C E R R
D A K I E O W N N R I C N O O
E E S P A R R O W R P T G T M
N S P A R T R I D G E S D S R
O L O E L G A E R E I G O X O
W O L L A W S C U C K O O Q C
```

◇ Bonus Trivia

Finish the quotation from Isaiah: "I will say to the north, Give up; and to the south, Keep not back."

"Bring my sons from far, and my daughters from the ends of the earth." (Isaiah 43:6)

167

Minerals and Gems of the Promised Land

ADAMANT

AGATE

ALABASTER

AMBER

AMETHYST

BERYL

BRIMSTONE

CARBUNCLE

CHRYSOPRASUS

COPPER

CORAL

CRYSTAL

DIAMOND

EMERALD

FLINT

GOLD

IRON

JACINTH

JASPER

LEAD

LIGURE

NITRE

ONYX

PEARL

QUARTZ

RUBY

SALT

SAPPHIRE

SARDINE

SARDONYX

SILVER

TIN

TOPAZ

```
Z S L E A D Z A P O T G S U L
T A L O S I J A C I N T H A N
R P A N U A R G L I G U R E R
A P Y L S L S O D D L O G U C
U H X P A F L I N T C R B A C
Q I E W R B A L L N U Y A T O
B R E T P M A G O V I K E E P
R E N O O T M S A B E T L X P
I D I N S T E E T T E R C Y E
M Y D Y Y D T V O E E E N N R
S X R F R E H N G O R L U O F
T C A P H Q Y R R T T E B D R
O R S R C X S J I C A L R R N
N R E B M A T N A M A D A A L
E M E R A L D L Y R E B C S B
```

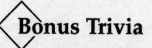 **Bonus Trivia**

What is Christ's question about spoiled salt?

"If the salt have lost his saltness, wherewith will ye season it?" (Mark 9:50)

168

Biblical Grains, Vegetables, and Seasonings

ALOE	GOURDS
ANISE	HYSSOP
BALSAM	LEEKS
BAY TREE	LENTILS
BDELLIUM	MALLOW
BEANS	MANDRAKES
CALAMUS	MILLET
CAMPHIRE	MUSTARD
CASSIA	MYRRH
CINNAMON	MYRTLE
CORIANDER	ONIONS
CORN	RUE
CUCUMBER	RYE
FRANKINCENSE	SPIKENARD
GALL	STACTE
GARLIC	WHEAT

```
H D M A N D R A K E S T N H T
P W L S H L B E R G E O R A R
E O C A L A M U S L M R E A C
E L J A L I L C L A Y H M E F
R L G S T R T I N M W U E R C
T A A H P A M N I X I E A I U
Y M W Y S I I D E L R N L H C
A I S S A C K S L L K Y O P U
B O K S N E T E D I R U E M M
A O E O P A D F N R A L O A B
R N E P A B E C B A U I F C E
C I L R A G E B Q N R O C O R
C O R I A N D E R I B D G V S
S N M U S T A R D S T A C T E
G S A E E R O N O E L T R Y M
```

⬦ Bonus Trivia

Finish the quotation, "In that he himself hath suffered being tempted—"

"He is able to succour them that are tempted." (Hebrews 2:18)

339

169

Old Testament Pagan Deities

ADRAMMELECH

AMON

AMON-RA

ASHERAH

ASHTOROTH

BAAL

BEL

BELIAL

BERITH

CHEMOSH

CHIUN

DAGON

EL

GAD

ISHTAR

ISIS

MARDUK

MENI

MERODACH

MILCOM

MOLECH

NEBO

NERGAL

PEOR

RIMMON

SIKKUTH

TERAPHIM

ZEBUL

```
S A G Z I N E M I L C O M R L
I I D A R P H A R E H S A E A
K A S S D O G O N E J S M M A
K F A I C H E M O S H S L E B
U W K S L R M P L T C Z C R C
T R K U D R A M O L E C H O H
H A A M O N T R J L C I D X
E T R D N I O S I D E O U A P
A H I D A T N B L M M K N C J
I S G R H N E R E A M Z J H T
Z I T W E L O R R C A O D R L
E D L R I B A N P T R G N M C
B S G A E E O U A I D A G O N
U A L N I M H A Z O A N G O G
L C M D A T E R A P H I M M Z
```

◇ **Bonus Trivia**

What is the rest of the verse in Deuteronomy beginning, "If from thence thou shalt seek the Lord thy God—"?

"Thou shalt find him, if thou seek him with all thy heart and with all thy soul." (Deuteronomy 4:29)

170

Paul's Third Missionary Journey: Cities, Regions, Nations

ACHAIA	JERUSALEM
ALEXANDRIA	LYSTRA
ANTIOCH	MACEDONIA
ASIA	MILETUS
ASSOS	MITYLENE
ATHENS	NEAPOLIS
BEREA	PATARA
CAESAREA	PHILIPPI
CHIOS	PHRYGIA
COOS	PTOLEMAIS
CYPRUS	RHODES
DERBE	SAMOS
EPHESUS	TARSUS
GALATIA	TROAS
ICONIUM	TYRE

```
M N S P M S O O P H R Y G I A
A O O A A E A D S U S R A T R
C I R O S E M N G M C S L A H
E Y R L M I L E T U S O A R O
D I P D N O A R L I C I T T D
O C A R N L O N R A O H I S E
N Y O R U A T H E N S C A Y S
I T A O S S X S N A N U H L A
A S Y O S T A E E S P R R C M
R O L R D R E B L T E O H E L
A S U S E H P E Y A H A L A J
T S E A R I T R T D I S I I L
A A E N B S E E I A S O M A S
P K R R E S I A M E L O T P Y
I C O N I U M P H I L I P P I
```

◇ Bonus Trivia

What saying of Christ's concerning His pre-existence introduces Abraham?

"Before Abraham was, I am." (John 8:58)

171

Titles of Jesus: Part One

ADAM

ADVOCATE

ALPHA AND OMEGA

AMEN

BEGINNING

BELOVED SON

BRANCH

CHIEF SHEPHERD

CHRIST

CORNERSTONE

DOOR

FINISHER

HOLY ONE

I AM

IMMANUEL

JUST ONE

KING OF KINGS

LAMB

LIFE

LIGHT OF THE WORLD

LORD OF ALL

MAN OF SORROWS

MESSIAH

OUR PASSOVER

RESURRECTION

ROCK

SAVIOR

VINE

WITNESS

```
B E L O V E D S O N H I C T D
S A A G E M O D N A A H P L A
Y G L R R E H S I N I F R R I
S D N I E E N S D E D O T E S
E W H I F S S O F O W R G V C
E T O I K E U S T E O N T O O
E S L R M F H R H S I R S S R
T I Y N R E O T R N U A S S N
A R O I P O F G N E V J E A E
C H N H E O S I N I C M N P R
O C E N T A G F O I A T T R S
V R I H D E O R O C K M I U T
D V G A B M B R A N C H W O O
A I M M A N U E L L A M B E N
L O R D O F A L L S A M E N E
```

Bonus Trivia

What is Paul's saying about "respect of persons"?

"There is no respect of persons with God." (Romans 2:11)

172
Biblical Trees

ACACIA
ALMOND
ALMUG
APPLE
ASH
BOX
CAROB
CEDAR
CHESTNUT
CYPRESS
EBONY
ELM
EVERGREEN
FIG
FIR

GOPHER
JUNIPER
MULBERRIES
OAK
OLIVE
PINE
PISTACHIO
POMEGRANATE
SHITTAH
SYCAMINE
SYCAMORE
TEIL
TEREBINTH
THYINE

```
A E N I P A H E I Y D B E L M
G C Y P R E S S D N O P N G W
P R A O S T A I O X J O U E N
T I C C A T C M T L I M T C E
O F D O I K L T F H L E Y C E
S H I T T A H I C A I G U H R
E H G U E Z G A C L H R I E G
I S T T M S T E L P P A G S R
R A S N C S Y L U B L N O T E
R A E N I M A C Y S U A P N V
E A D P E B O C A N L T H U E
B H E E G C E L A M O E E T A
L U Q I C G T R I R O B R Q S
U R E P I N U J E V O R E C G
M K D I E N I Y H T E B E M A
```

Bonus Trivia

What is the proverb about pride and a fall?

"Pride goeth before destruction, and an haughty spirit before a fall." (Proverbs 16:18)

347

173
Satanic Synonyms

ABADDON	FATHER OF LIES
ACCUSER	GOD OF THIS AGE
ADVERSARY	LIAR
ANGEL OF LIGHT	LUCIFER
ANOINTED CHERUB	MURDERER
APOLLYON	ROARING LION
BEELZEBUB	RULER OF DARKNESS
BELIAL	SATAN
DECEIVER	SERPENT
DEVIL	STRONG MAN
DRAGON	TEMPTER
ENEMY	THIEF
EVIL ONE	WICKED ONE

```
B U R E H C D E T N I O N A S
S R E T P M E T L I V E D S E
T G O D O F T H I S A G E S I
R N E N O L I V E B N N C W L
O O L A I L E B A R K S E I F
N Y I B M U R D E R E R I C O
G L E U A C D F A R A R V K R
M L N B I O I D P C K V E E E
A O E E N C F E R S C A R D H
N P M Z U O N E A A F U R O T
O A Y L R T V T I U G L S N A
A D V E R S A R Y H A O I E F
I S L E Z N F Z O V T G N A R
E U G B N O I L G N I R A O R
R C H A N G E L O F L I G H T
```

◇ **Bonus Trivia**

Finish the promise in Leviticus, "Ye shall lie down—"

"And none shall make you afraid."
(Leviticus 26:6)

174

Old Testament Authors

AGUR	JEREMIAH
AMOS	JESUS
ASAPH	JONAH
DANIEL	JOSHUA
DAVID	KING LEMUEL
ETHAN	MALACHI
EZEKIEL	MICAH
EZRA	MOSES
GOD	NAHUM
HABUKKUK	OBADIAH
HAGGAI	SAMUEL
HEMAN	SOLOMON
HOLY SPIRIT	SONS OF KORAH
HOSEA	UNKNOWN
ISAIAH	ZECHARIAH
JEDUTHUN	ZEPHANIAH

```
I R Y H A I N A H P E Z D I O
C H I S C R D O M U H A N B N
N S A S B I O L L S N R A O R
U P R I H A G G A I U D M E P
H M Z E A O E R E G I O E J L
T A E C B S L L A A L T H E E
U L R R U T I Y H O H O U R U
D A I O K L E W S A S M E E M
E C U N K N O W N P A P Z M E
J H D D U F M T Y S I M E I L
D I A V K A O I L G U R K A G
A R H E A O M S C C H S I H N
V A U H S O J O N A H W E T I
I G O M M O S E S O H A L J K
D H A I R A H C E Z S K H U C
```

◇ Bonus Trivia

In what book is the prayer, "Lead me to the rock that is higher than I"?

Psalms (61:2)

175

Titles of Jesus:
Part Two:

ARM OF THE LORD	MORNING STAR
AUTHOR	PRINCE OF PEACE
BREAD OF LIFE	PROPHET
BUILDER	ROOT
CREATOR	SERVANT
FIRST	SHILOH
GOOD SHEPHERD	SON
HEAD	SON OF DAVID
HORN OF SALVATION	SON OF MAN
IMAGE OF GOD	STONE
JEHOVAH	SURETY
JUST	TRUTH
LAST	WAY
LEADER	WORD
LIGHT	

```
L T T D H L P N E H A D M R E
I F A T E R A O Y O R R O D E
G E U A O M L I A O M E R O C
H R D P F O I T W L O D N G A
T E H O B R E A D O F L I F E
R E N R S E R V A N T I N O P
T O O S T W N L H L H U G E F
S O T M H A T A S F E B S G O
T N A A U I V S S T L L T A E
T K T T E O L F U U O W A M C
Q S H S H R R O F J R N R I N
U O A E R T C N H N D E E C I
R D J L B I T R H L O U T E R
R D I V A D F O N O S S U Y P
C A G O O D S H E P H E R D N
```

◇ Bonus Trivia

Who said to a mighty king, "Let thy gifts be to thyself, and give thy rewards to another"?

Daniel to Belshazzar (Daniel 5:17)

176

Bible Translators: 1526–1787

AINSWORTH	MORTIMER
BARBAR	MACKNIGHT
BATLY	PARKER
BLAYNEY	PURVER
COVERDALE	STARNHOLD
CARYLL	SCOTT
CHANDLER	SMART
CALLENDER	TYNDALE
DODDRIDGE	TAVERNER
HAAK	WAKEFIELD
HOPKINS	WHITTINGHAM
HORWOOD	WHISTON
JOYE	WYNNE
LEWIS	WORSLEY
LOWTH	

```
H B U E D L E I F E K A W H W
S S C A L L E N D E R H O R D
O M V Y A Y M E X E I R R E V
T M A D Y R A S Y T W D S K E
O T N R H A C X T O U P L R L
S Y O M T C K I O O J U E A A
T T M C H A N D L E R V Y P D
A S A R S G I W A E R M U G R
V Y D R H O G M M U W Y N N E
E H L A N K H I P L E W I S V
R T M T I H T R O W S N I A O
N W R Y A R O R A B R A B Y C
E O W A O B A L S N I K P O H
R L K M K D O D D R I D G E D
B L A Y N E Y Y N O T S I H W
```

◇ Bonus Trivia

To whom did the Lord say, "Speak unto the children of Israel, that they go forward"?

Moses (Exodus 14:15)

355

177

Men in "Acts" ion: Paul's Partners

AGABUS	LUKE
ANANIAS	MANAEN
APOLLOS	MARK
AQUILA	MATTHIAS
ARISTARCHUS	PETER
BARNABAS	PHILIP
CORNELIUS	SECUNDUS
CRISPUS	SILAS
ERASTUS	SIMEON
GAIUS	SOPATER
JAMES	STEPHEN
JASON	TIMOTHY
JOHN	TROPHIMUS
LUCIUS	TYCHICUS

S	S	E	C	U	N	D	U	S	V	N	H	W	O	S
G	U	U	O	M	D	P	I	T	U	G	O	K	E	E
O	T	S	M	J	A	N	R	E	T	I	R	S	S	M
O	S	O	M	I	O	N	E	P	L	A	A	A	A	A
S	A	L	I	S	H	H	A	H	M	N	B	G	A	J
L	R	L	U	I	U	P	N	E	A	A	G	R	T	H
S	E	O	B	K	O	E	O	N	N	M	I	R	Y	N
S	O	P	A	T	E	R	I	R	A	S	E	P	C	O
L	Q	A	Y	R	N	A	A	T	T	T	Z	H	H	E
G	U	O	Q	D	S	B	T	A	E	F	N	I	I	M
A	G	A	B	U	S	H	R	P	C	H	C	L	C	I
T	F	O	P	B	I	C	O	R	N	E	L	I	U	S
E	U	L	J	A	H	L	U	C	I	U	S	P	S	H
A	H	T	S	U	N	A	A	Y	H	T	O	M	I	T
S	X	S	S	U	P	S	I	R	C	U	I	C	U	L

◇ Bonus Trivia

In whose song are the words, "He hath put down the mighty from their seats, and exalted them of low degree"?

Mary's (Luke 1:52)

357

178
Biblical Diseases

APHASIA

APOPLEXY

BLAINS

BLEMISHES

BLINDNESS

BOILS

CANCER

CONSUMPTION

DEPRESSION

DYSENTERY

EDEMA

EPILEPSY

FEVER

GANGRENE

GOUT

HEARING LOSS

LAMENESS

LEPROSY

MALARIA

PALSY

PLAGUE

POLIO

RINGWORM

SMALLPOX

SUNSTROKE

SYNCOPE

TUBERCULOSIS

WORMS

```
M E N E R G N A G F E V E R A
R S O D I W L E P R O S Y I P
O B I Y E E L K R H L L R A N
W L T S T P N I B I A A L O I
G I P E O I A I O M L S I O S
N N M N R L E B E A Y S I A L
I D U T A E U N M N S L M A E
R N S E C P E C C E O E R G K
E E N R N S O O R P D R O S O
C S O Y S Y P P W E N U G N R
N S C S A E E L L O B E O I T
A A C N E D T C A E R U U A S
C S E H S I M E L B X M T L N
S S O L G N I R A E H Y S B U
P L A G U E H X O P L L A M S
```

◇ Bonus Trivia

What is Paul's saying contrasting the letter and the spirit?

"The letter killeth, but the spirit giveth life."
(2 Corinthians 3:6)

179

David's Mighty Men

ABI-ALBON	HELEB
ABIEZER	HELEZ
ABISHAI	HEZRAI
ADINO	HIDDAI
AHIAM	IGAL
ASAHEL	IRA
AZMAVETH	ITTAI
BANI	JONATHAN
BENAIAH	MAHARAI
ELEAZAR	MEBUNNAI
ELHANAN	NAHARAI
ELIAHBA	PAARAI
ELIAM	SHAMMAH
ELIKA	URIAH
ELIPHELET	ZALMON
GAREB	ZELEK

```
M O J R A Z E L E K P Z I A A
A U O A C E L I K A C H A D Z
I D N Z B D R H A B I E Z E R
H I A A A I W R W N R R L D A
A A T E N A A P E P N E A A X
N D H L I I D L I M H U N N T
T D A E A L I Y B A A A B H T
S I N T E A N A I O H I S E E
B H T H H N O G R A N S L L M
E I A B O D A J R A V E I E M
R S A M E L N A N A H L E B L
A R L R M H I H O P E A K A A
G A F N C A H A I R U R M Y C
Z I A R Z E H L B E N A I A H
S A M S H T E V A M Z A R E J
```

Bonus Trivia

Finish Peter's saying, "One day is with the Lord as a thousand years—"

"And a thousand years as one day."
(2 Peter 3:8)

180

Women of the Bible

ABIGAIL	MICHAL
ASENATH	NAOMI
BATHSHEBA	PHOEBE
DEBORAH	PRISCILLA
DELILAH	RACHEL
DINAH	RAHAB
ELISABETH	REBEKAH
ESTHER	RHODA
EUNICE	RUTH
EVE	SALOME
JEZEBEL	SAPPHIRA
LEAH	SARAH
LOIS	TABITHA
MARTHA	TAMAR
MARY	

```
B L E B E Z E J A R M I K O R
A W T O B V M I C H A L S L A
H U S N E T L O H C S E A I N
A T I S O A T H I H M H R A E
R M E A H T R A M R A C A G C
I A G B P O D E B O R A H I I
E L F A A R N L B I Y R D B N
D L U T E S H A C E T S B A U
O I C H A N I D O S K H I D E
K C T S L S A L O M E A A O P
L S E H C D T X E S I B H H L
E I Z E S A P P H I R A F R T
N R A B M G A B O X G L U Q O
T P H A L I L E D K I T B O R
J O R M A S E N A T H E A M P
```

181
Preachers & Evangelists of Today

Max ANDERS	Richard LEE
James BOICE	Erwin LUTZER
Stuart BRISCOE	John MACARTHUR
Dave BURNHAM	Stephen OLFORD
Joseph CHAMBERS	John PHILLIPS
Richard EUTSLER	Derek PRINCE
Tony EVANS	Perry F. ROCKWOOD
Billy GRAHAM	J. Harold SMITH
Ben HADEN	Charles STANLEY
David HOCKING	Lehman STRAUSS
Ron HUTCHCRAFT	Chuck SWINDOLL
Jack HYLES	Warren WIERSBE
Greg LAURIE	

```
R E L G N I K C O H G M I D C
A U P W E A D R E Z T U L F S
M A H A R G O S K C T R S I B
G E I T U D O E Z F O E E W S
O S L Y R T W I A Q A L B M R
E V L M O A K R U O H S I Y E
B U I B L I C U D S D T W S B
S H P C R H O A O R H U B W M
R N S G C I R L M E S E O I A
E B A T P E S A L D T V I N H
I M U V A J H C K N R E C D C
W H A D E N P U O A A O E O A
E C N I R P L H G E U W F L S
T D I U C K C E J C S R I L F
A O B E N S E L Y H S O B A O
```

◇ **Bonus Trivia**

In what Book is the great affirmation, "Hear,
O Israel: The Lord our God is one Lord"?

Deuteronomy (6:4)

182

Preachers & Evangelists of Yesteryear

Hyman J. APPELMAN
(1902-1983)

Donald BARNHOUSE
(1895-1960)

J. Wilbur CHAPMAN
(1859-1918)

M.R. DEHAAN (1891-1965)

A.C. DIXON (1854-1925)

Jonathan EDWARDS
(1703-1758)

Charles G. FINNEY
(1792-1875)

Arno C. GAEBELEIN
(1861-1945)

A.J. GORDON (1836-1895)

Oliver B. GREENE
(1915-1976)

H.A. IRONSIDE (1876-1951)

Clarence LARKIN (1850-1924)

R.G. LEE (1886-1978)

Martyn LLOYD-JONES
(1899-1981)

Herbert LOCKYER
(1886-1984)

Alexander MACLAREN
(1826-1910)

J. Vernon McGEE (1904-1988)

F.B. MEYER (1847-1929)

Dwight L. MOODY
(1837-1899)

G. Campbell MORGAN
(1863-1945)

John R. RICE (1895-1980)

J.C. RYLE (1816-1900)

J. Oswald SANDERS
(1902-1992)

Charles SPURGEON
(1834-1892)

Billy SUNDAY (1862-1935)

R.A. TORREY (1856-1928)

A.W. TOZER (1897-1963)

George W. TRUETT
(1867-1944)

John WESLEY (1703-1791)

George WHITEFIELD
(1714-1770)

```
W A S H G E N A M L E P P A N
H D L C T S M E Y G N M L E R
I P I R A E C S R A B O B M O
T N J X Y S G E A A C D S L S
E O C E O L E H R K L C O A G
F E R N W N E N Y D H C N I C
I G N R E D H E O O Z D A H E
E R I C E O R X L J E E A M N
L U E R U Y J T G R D P C O I
D P L S O T E N S W M Y W H K
O S E F O N O N A A D A O S R
B A B Z S D S R N O K D E L A
T T E U R T D I O I X N G O L
I R A O D S J M D T F U R N D
N A G R O M K E Y E L S E W O
```

Bonus Trivia

Who asked the question, "Shall we receive good at the hand of God, and shall we not receive evil"?

Job (Job 2:10)

183
Names and Titles of Jesus Christ

ALPHA

CHRIST

DEITY

DELIVERER

DOOR

GOD

GREAT SHEPHERD

HIGH PRIEST

HOLY ONE

IMMANUEL

JESUS

KING OF KINGS

LAMB

LIFE

LIGHT

LION

LORD

MESSIAH

OMEGA

PRINCE OF PEACE

PROPHET

REDEEMER

ROCK

SAVIOUR

SON OF GOD

TRUE VINE

TRUTH

WAY

WORD

```
A D E L I V E R E R A H P L A
W U R C O H K N T D R O I E R
E O G E W R I F O B W F C U I
K L R A H V D G A M E A O N H
C I Y D E P F N H R E I J A A
O G N U V O E O L P V G L M I
T H R G N T L H F A R J A M S
R T A O O Y G O S E M I H I S
E E S H O F E B U T C B E U E
M H C N K C K Q E R A D S S M
E P E C N H D I A D H E D M T
E O O I S R N O N O J I R H R
D R R F M I O A O G U T O G U
E P L I T S I L E R S Y A L T
R U S N E T L O H C S I S D H
```

◇ Bonus Trivia

What proverb about grapes did Ezekiel refute?

"The fathers have eaten sour grapes, and the children's teeth are set on edge."
(Ezekiel 18:2)

369

184

Noah's Flood

ARK

BEASTS

BIRD

CATTLE

COMMANDED

DOVE

EARTH

FEMALE

FLOOD

FORTY

FOWLS

GOD

HAM

HEAVEN

HOUSE

JAPHETH

LIFE

MALE

NOAH

RAIN

SHEM

TWO

VIOLENCE

WATER

WOOD

```
G D F L O O D S C T R F O B A
X O P N L I O T R A G O D L R
P C D D K E V X T D T R H I K
O G N G R I E O W V I T P S I
B Z R O D P O R O B S Y L T K
C O M M A N D E D N L C R E J
W O O D M H L I S H E M K A A
A R I N W E T W D O B N S R P
T L F X M A L E N U Y T T T H
E J E H O V M L K S A I O H E
R K M U F E L I F E L H B R T
L A A X O N F R A M R A I N H
M T L V I R E V I I B M S N V
Z I E V I O L E N C E F R E O
F O W L S X D Y C B E A S T S
```

Bonus Trivia

Who did Christ say are His brother, His sister, and His mother?

"Whosoever shall do the will of my Father which is in heaven." (Matthew 12:50)

185

Moses' Mission

AFFLICTION
BURNING
BUSH
CRY
EGYPT
FIRE
FLAME
FLOCK
GENERATION
GOLD
HONEY
ISRAEL
JEWELS
JOURNEY

LAND
LORD
MILK
MOSES
MOUNTAIN
PEOPLE
PHARAOH
SACRIFICE
SILVER
SMITE
SORROW
WILDERNESS
WONDERS

```
M K C A F F L I C T I O N K P
O O B G Z L A C R X G L H W H
S Z U E K A N F Y K E R I F A
E M S N P M D H E A B L E L R
S U H E T E T X R F D C M P A
T M U R R A R S O E I Q S R O
X O I A I C I O R F Y E N O H
S U B T B U R N I N G T V U X
R N M I E L E R Y M R S Z S W
P T Q O U S C F P E Z O N R S
M A S N S A L D V L N R W E L
O I V D S O R L R P W R O D E
U N L T C A I Q I O V O U N W
Z O X K Z S Q I F E L W X O E
G T Y B A I E G Y P T A C W J
```

186
Plagues Strike Egypt

AARON	HEART
ANIMALS	HORDES
BLOOD	LAND
BOILS	LICE
DARKNESS	LIVESTOCK
DEATH	LOCUSTS
DECEITFUL	MOSES
DUST	OBEY
EGYPT	PHARAOH
FIRSTBORN	RIVER
FLIES	ROD
FROGS	SERPENT
HAIL	SICK
HAND	SWARMS

```
D F X B L O O D O T Q Y H B S
C E Z I Q K C I S O E R O E W
K O C X B T B U G B S E R U A
O E M E R O D S O G M P D L R
B G H F I X P T O X E O E I M
O Q A Q V T C R L N Y T S V S
I Y I A E A F C T Q E D S E B
L T L R R W L U M X V E T S S
S E Y I S O S H L T I A Y T L
L G R S C T N Q O L L T S O A
S Y E U R X D M F A R H Q C M
M P S A U V F G N S R D H K I
T T E C H A N D B X Z A B O N
S H O N R O B T S R I F H G A
B D A R K N E S S Q P M T P P
```

Bonus Trivia

Give the sentence from the Revelation which ends, "and their works do follow them."

"Blessed are the dead which die in the Lord from henceforth: Yea, saith the Spirit, that they may rest from their labours; and their works do follow them." (Revelation 14:13)

187

Whole Armour of God

ARMOUR

BLOOD

BREASTPLATE

DARTS

DEVIL

FAITH

FEET

FLESH

GIRT

GOD

GOSPEL

HELMET

LIONS

PEACE

PRAYER

PRINCIPALITIES

QUENCH

RIGHTEOUSNESS

SAINTS

SALVATION

SHIELD

SHOD

SPIRITUAL

SWORD

TRUTH

WRESTLE

```
H S E L F U D E V I L V G O D
S A L V A T I O N W S I T S B
E I M X O L A U T I R I P S G
I N D A R T S O R T B L M E C
T T H F E E T T E R N E V N E
I S J A M T K E Y P Q P U S Q
L A E I F K A M A Z X S H U U
A F L T C E R L R S T O V O E
P G T H O X M E P W D G Z E N
I V S R T V O H X T N O L T C
C L E H U W U L D S S G X H H
N I R D I T R Q F W N A F G B
I M W F S E H B O A C O E I Q
R Q H B Z R L R S B Q T I R E
P E A C E X D D U M D O O L B
```

Bonus Trivia

To what does the proverb compare pleasant words?

"Pleasant words are as an honeycomb, sweet to the soul, and health to the bones."
(Proverbs 16:24)

188

Books of the Bible: Part 1:

GENESIS

EXODUS

LEVITICUS

NUMBERS

DEUTERONOMY

JOSHUA

JUDGES

RUTH

SAMUEL

KINGS

CHRONICLES

EZRA

NEHEMIAH

ESTHER

JOB

PSALMS

PROVERBS

ECCLESIASTES

(SONG OF) SOLOMON

ISAIAH

JEREMIAH

LAMENTATIONS

EZEKIEL

DANIEL

```
L X R Y M O N O R E T U E D T
B A N U M B E R S S P I O S M
D T M L E I N A D T E Q A J E
A O N E H E M I A H T F I X P
C X Z Y N L E I K E Z E O R Q
S R J A S T R V P R O D Z L J
A S U E L O A S L N U P M E O
M I D T Q P T Q S O R R V B
U S G C H R O N I C L E S I X
E E E F A O S O L O M O N T A
L N S D I V Z J K I N G S I U
Z E N S A E M F A X R S O C H
F G F J S R V H T M Q B D U S
C X M O I B S M L A S P I S O
E C C L E S I A S T E S R E J
```

◇ **Bonus Trivia**

Finish the words of the psalm, "My soul,
wait thou only upon God; for—"

"My expectation is from him." (Psalm 62:5)

189

Books of the Bible: Part 2

HOSEA	JOHN
JOEL	ACTS
AMOS	ROMANS
OBADIAH	CORINTHIANS
JONAH	COLOSSIANS
MICAH	THESSALONIANS
NAHUM	TIMOTHY
HABAKKUK	TITUS
ZEPHANIAH	PHILEMON
HAGGAI	HEBREWS
ZECHARIAH	JAMES
MALACHI	PETER
MATTHEW	JUDE
MARK	REVELATION
LUKE	

```
T I M O T H Y I C P E T E R Z
Q H Z M P H I L E M O N C E E
P E E X L K Y D J A M E S V C
I B P S B L J X O B A D I A H
H R H N S O I O H R C K X N A
C E A B E A Q L N O R L M O R
A W N L G E L K L A N E S I I
L S I G U I U O M Q H D N T A
A Y A O N K S W N K E U A A H
M H H S K S E N E I L J M L B
I Z T A I P A K Q H A T O E Y
C C B A S M E P M X T N R V Z
A A N X O Y S S U T I T S E T
H S R S T Z O L X Y B O A R R
C O R I N T H I A N S I E M S
```

Bonus Trivia

To whom was it said, "Dust thou art, and unto dust shalt thou return"?

To Adam, by God (Genesis 3:19)

190
Women in the Bible

ABIGAIL	LEAH
ABITAL	LOIS
ACHSAH	LYDIA
AHINOAM	MAACHAH
ANNA	MARTHA
BATHSHEBA	MICHAL
BATHSHUA	MIRIAM
CANDACE	NAARAH
DEBORAH	NAOMI
DORCAS	ORPAH
EGLAH	PHOEBE
ELIZABETH	PRISCILLA
ESTHER	RACHEL
EUNICE	RAHAB
EVE	REBEKAH
HAGGITH	RUTH
HANNAH	SARAH
HELAH	TABITHA
HERODIAS	TAMAR
JEZEBEL	

```
B A T H S H E B A E C I N U E
A S A I D O R E H M A I D Y L
T H A R O B E D O R C A S E I
H A K E B E R R P H O E B E Z
S T A B I T H A N N A E V E A
H E C A D N A C A R Z Y T H B
U E M E R U T H R E H T S E E
A B I G A I L E J R A M A T T
H O B L C T M L H N A O M I H
T L A A H E A O E R O A A H A
I A H H S F O I J A R H I A N
G T A E A S N S U T H A R P N
G I R S H M I C H A L R I R A
A B H E L A H A H C A A M O H
H A R A A N A L L I C S I R P
```

Bonus Trivia

Complete the war cry, "The sword of the Lord—"

"And of Gideon." (Judges 7:18)

191

Men in the Bible

AARON	JOSHUA
ABEL	JUDAS
ABRAHAM	LAMECH
ADAM	LOT
AHAB	LUKE
AMOS	MARK
ANDREW	MATTHEW
BARTHOLOMEW	NEBUCHADNEZZAR
CALEB	NICODEMUS
DAVID	NOAH
ESAU	PAUL
GIDEON	PETER
HOSEA	PHILIP
HUR	PILATE
ISAAC	SAMUEL
JACOB	SAUL
JAMES	SIMON
JEHOSHAPHAT	SOLOMON
JOHN	TERAH
JONAH	THADDEUS
JONATHAN	THOMAS

```
J O N A T H A N W E H T T A M
A E J O S H U A M A H A R B A
M S H E T A L I P O M A R K W
E A N O A H N O M O L O S E W
S U J E S S A M U E L M T E
I S A A C H S L E B A O E H R
M R H O S E A H A B L R J A D
O U D A V I D P U O A M O D N
N H O J U D A S H H S A N D A
O P N A M O S T T A C D A E P
E E O C H R R O I S T A H U A
D T R O C A L E B T L U A S U
I E A B B L A M E C H E K U L
G R A Z Z E N D A H C U B E N
N I C O D E M U S P H I L I P
```

Bonus Trivia

Who said, "We will give ourselves
continually to prayer, and to the ministry of
the word"?

The apostles (Acts 6:4)

192

Cities in Palestine

ANTIPATRIS

ARIMATHEA

ASHKELON

BETHANY

BETHLEHEM

BETHSAIDA

CAESAREA

CANA

CAPERNAUM

EMMAUS

EPHRAIM

GAZA

GERASA

HEBRON

HERODIUM

JERICHO

JERUSALEM

JOPPA

LYDDA

MAGDALA

NAIN

NAZARETH

SAMARIA

SIDON

SYCHAR

TYRE

```
C A D I A S H T E B A P P O J
B A A C E I E H S I D O N E K
E B E F D G B J N A I N R H L
T M A S N T R O R T M I A T C
H E E U A Y O Q P S C R L E A
L L H V W R N B X H L A A R N
E A T A Z E E Y O C Y H D A A
H S A B E T H A N Y D C G Z D
E U M E A S A R E G D Y A A F
M R I G Z A I R A M A S M N H
I E R J A S I R T A P I T N A
M J A L G C A P E R N A U M K
N E P H R A I M O S U A M M E
A S H K E L O N A E J I D Q P
H L F B H E R O D I U M C G K
```

Bonus Trivia

Who said of marriage, "What therefore God hath joined together, let not man put asunder"?

Christ (Mark 10:9)

193

Books of the New Testament

MATTHEW	TIMOTHY
MARK	TITUS
LUKE	PHILEMON
JOHN	HEBREWS
ACTS	JAMES
ROMANS	PETER
CORINTHIANS	FIRST JOHN
GALATIANS	SECOND JOHN
EPHESIANS	THIRD JOHN
PHILIPPIANS	JUDE
COLOSSIANS	REVELATION
THESSALONIANS	

C	C	A	B	C	M	A	T	T	H	E	W	D	Z	E
F	O	T	H	E	S	S	A	L	O	N	I	A	N	S
G	L	R	H	S	N	A	I	P	P	I	L	I	H	P
I	O	F	I	R	E	V	E	L	A	T	I	O	N	J
K	S	I	P	N	L	O	Q	S	V	S	M	U	X	P
A	S	R	H	B	T	C	E	D	U	J	E	K	U	L
S	I	S	I	N	Y	H	D	T	R	E	P	W	N	Y
T	A	T	L	F	H	G	I	T	H	I	H	J	H	K
C	N	J	E	L	T	T	M	A	N	P	E	H	O	O
A	S	O	M	Q	O	R	T	S	N	U	S	E	J	S
S	V	H	O	X	M	A	R	K	Y	S	I	B	D	N
E	A	N	N	W	I	C	G	K	E	I	A	R	R	A
M	D	H	R	E	T	E	P	J	L	Z	N	E	I	M
A	O	N	H	O	J	D	N	O	C	E	S	W	H	O
J	B	H	F	G	A	L	A	T	I	A	N	S	T	R

◁ Bonus Trivia

Finish the verse of the psalm, "O thou that hearest prayer—"

"Unto thee shall all flesh come." (Psalm 65:2)

194

Books of the Old Testament

GENESIS

EXODUS

LEVITICUS

NUMBERS

DEUTERONOMY

JOSHUA

JUDGES

RUTH

SAMUEL

KINGS

CHRONICLES

EZRA

NEHEMIAH

ESTHER

JOB

PSALMS

ECCLESIASTES

SONG OF SOLOMON

ISAIAH

JEREMIAH

LAMENTATIONS

EZEKIEL

DANIEL

JOEL

AMOS

OBADIAH

JONAH

NAHUM

HABAKKUK

ZEPHANIAH

HAGGAI

ZECHARIAH

MALACHI

E	C	C	L	E	S	I	A	S	T	E	S	E	T	Z
Y	M	O	N	O	R	E	T	U	E	D	S	X	I	E
A	H	L	E	I	N	A	D	N	E	E	N	O	S	C
M	S	U	C	I	T	I	V	E	L	Z	O	D	A	H
O	J	O	E	L	E	S	T	H	E	R	I	U	I	A
S	S	O	M	U	H	A	N	E	O	A	T	S	A	R
H	A	B	A	K	K	U	K	M	A	L	A	C	H	I
A	M	A	R	U	T	H	I	I	J	S	T	S	A	A
I	U	D	L	D	T	S	N	A	U	M	N	I	I	H
N	E	I	E	S	T	O	G	H	D	L	E	S	M	A
A	L	A	A	J	M	J	S	E	G	A	M	E	E	G
H	C	H	R	O	N	I	C	L	E	S	A	N	R	G
P	S	R	E	B	M	U	N	N	S	P	L	E	E	A
E	Z	E	K	I	E	L	H	A	N	O	J	G	J	I
Z	T	N	O	M	O	L	O	S	F	O	G	N	O	S

<diamond> **Bonus Trivia**

Who said, "I am doing a great work, so that I cannot come down"?

Nehemiah (Nehemiah 6:3)

195

Names of Jesus

ALL (IN ALL)

ALPHA

BRANCH

BREAD

BRIDEGROOM

CHRIST

COUNSELOR

DOOR

EMMANUEL

FRIEND

GOD

GOOD SHEPHERD

JESUS

LAMB

LIFE

LIGHT

LORD OF LORDS

MESSIAH

OMEGA

PRIEST

PRINCE OF PEACE

REDEEMER

RESURRECTION

ROCK

ROSE (OF SHARON)

SAVIOUR

SON OF GOD

SON OF MAN

(MORNING) STAR

THE MIGHTY GOD

TRUTH

VINE

WAY

WONDERFUL

WORD

(LIVING) WATER

```
T K H L O R D O F L O R D S N
H B C I S R O L E S N U O C A
E R N G I U A H P L A W M N M
M I A H G O S L I F E O E N F
I D R T R E D E E M E R G O O
G E B W A T E R J F K D A I N
H G O O D S H E P H E R D T O
T R L U F R E D N O W T A C S
Y O E D N E I R F W E R E E A
G O U P R I E S T A S U R R V
O M N D O O R S I Y O T B R I
D R A N G V I K C O R H G U O
L A M B I R D O G F O N O S U
L T M N H A I S S E M S D E R
A S E C A E P F O E C N I R P
```

Bonus Trivia

Finish the proverb, "Trust in the Lord with all thy heart; and—"

"Lean not unto thine own understanding." (Proverbs 3:5)

196

Joseph

ASENATH	JACOB
BAKER	KINE
BASKETS	MIDIANITES
BUTLER	MONEY
CAMELS	MOON
COAT	NUTS
CUP	PIT
DIE	POTI-PHERAH
DOTHAN	PRISON
DREAMER	RACHEL
EGYPT	SHEAVES
EMBALM	SHECHEM
FORGIVE	SUN
FORTY	VINE
GOSHEN	ZAPHNATH-PAANEAH
HEBREW	

```
L T F O R G I V E H T P Y G E
S U S A H O M Y N U P R O I K
E H T Z U S E T I N A I D I M
V D E I T H S R V I N M O G K
A I K C P E O O H S L O R I I
E U S T U N H F E A L O N U R
H T A N E S A I B G F E G E P
S D B V B H R M Y E N O M R P
R R I U O A E K I N S A O A U
W E A O C S H E C H E M N P C
E A K H A E P O A R U C O A T
R E E A J T I Z D I M P S I K
B L S U B U T L E R O A I U I
E S N A H T O D M P O Z R O N
H A E N A A P H T A N H P A Z
```

◇ Bonus Trivia

To what did Paul compare the coming of "the day of the Lord"?

"As a thief in the night." (1 Thessalonians 5:2)

197

Jacob

ASHER	LADDER
BETHUEL	LEAH
BILHAH	LENTILES
BIRTHRIGHT	LEVI
CANAAN	LUZ
DAN	MANDRAKES
DINAH	NAPHTALI
EAST	OIL
ESAU	PADANARAM
FLOCKS	RACHEL
GAD	REBEKAH
GOD ALMIGHTY	RODS
ISAAC	VOW
ISSACHAR	WELL
JOSEPH	ZEBULUN
LABAN	ZILPAH

```
N A B A L B I R A H C A S S I
A S E I E W O V E L U O R A E
P H T A R S G J E V I L Y S L
H A H S O T O S E L I T N E L
T D U J D I H B E Z H W A Z A
A D E A S T I R E G I H A K D
L E L A N E A B I S H A N I D
I D A G C C K M A G A N A C E
B C N A H E L A D S H L U Z R
Z A R E B A U L R R K T S E A
I N L I D F L O E D L C B B D
L A J O S E P H J E N E O U A
P A G V W O S B S R K A F L P
A N A D P A D A N A R A M U F
H A H L I B U L H H T E B N Z
```

◇ **Bonus Trivia**

Of whom is it said in Hebrews that of them "the world was not worthy"?

(8ε:ΙΙ sʍǝɹqǝH)
ɥʇıɐɟ ɟo uǝɯoʍ puɐ uǝɯ ʇuǝɯɐʇsǝ⊥ plO ǝɥ⊥

198

Abraham

ALTAR	KETURAH
ANGEL	LORD
BETHEL	LOT
CATTLE	MACHPELAH
CAVE	MAMRE
CHALDEES	MELCHIZEDEK
CIRCUMCISION	MORIAH
ELIEZER	NAHOR
GOMORRAH	PHILISTINES
HAGAR	SARAH
HAI	SODOM
HARAN	SON
HEBREW	TERAH
ISAAC	UR
ISHMAEL	ZOAR

```
M H A R A S C A L E G N A O Z
T A S E N I T S I L I H P S Z
E R M A R W R B E T S O D O M
K R H R B E O N K T N L A N A
E O I L E R M O G A G R C L C
D M A M O B R I H C A T T H H
E O N H V E A S B P L A O A P
Z G A A M H S I L E R E L S E
I N C R R R H C A L T A T E L
H A R U E A L M L M I H P E A
C H A T R A H U O C A V E D H
L E O E H S I C R R C M O L E
E B T K I H A R D O I R H A I
M R O C A A S I E G N A I H H
E L I E Z E R C R A G A H C P
```

Bonus Trivia

What is the saying in Hosea about being "joined to idols"?

"Ephraim is joined to idols: let him alone." (Hosea 4:17)

199

Prophets

ABRAHAM	JEHU
AGABUS	JEREMIAH
AHIJAH	JOEL
AMOS	JOHN
BALAAM	JONAH
BARNABAS	MALACHI
DANIEL	MICAH
DAVID	MICAIAH
DEBORAH	MOSES
ELIJAH	NAHUM
ELISHA	NATHAN
EZEKIEL	OBADIAH
GAD	PAUL
HAGGAI	SAMUEL
HOSEA	SIMEON
ISAIAH	ZEPHANIAH

```
L S A B A N R A B A D L S O H
E I H B E D H S U H E J H A J
I M S U R I F U Z U H O I K O
K E U A J O H B M B C M J M H
E O P A I M U A G A E O O A N
Z N H K P A S G M R Z S N M A
E I A G G A H A E N E Z A U T
D A N I E L H J D S C O H H H
O B A D I A H O M I C A H A A
A S I M R B G C L P V P I N N
H D E B O R A H E E E A L A B
S I A S I S A I O Z C U D A G
I S A E S O H A J I L E G O A
L U A P B A L A M A L A C H I
E F H A I N A H P E Z G I N S
```

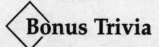

Bonus Trivia

What command follows "Cease to do evil"?

"Learn to do well." (Isaiah 1:16–17)

401

200

Christ's Passion

ANNAS	KINGDOM
BARABBAS	LANTERNS
BETRAYED	LAW
CAIAPHAS	LINEN
CEDRON	MALCHUS
CHIEF PRIESTS	OFFICERS
COCK	PHARISEES
CROWN	PURPLE
CRUCIFY	SCOURGED
CUP	SIMON
DAMSEL	SOLDIERS
DISCIPLES	SON
JEWS	SYNAGOGUE
JUDAS	TEMPLE
JUDGMENT HALL	TORCHES

```
N O M I S O M I S I M U O C S
F A N J A B F A E E L P M E T
M O D G N I K F L E S M A D S
C A I P N C S O P C E U J I E
B E T R A Y E D I R H D E S I
A U D I N W O R C U C U W D R
R G S R F L I L S C R J S E P
O O A W O A M A I I O E I G F
F G B N R N H N D F T K M R E
F A B C U P O T N Y S I C U I
I N A S A F W E L P R U P O H
C Y R I P H A R I S E E S C C
E S A D U J L N E N I L A S R
R C B E T E M S O L D I E R S
S O N L L A H T N E M G D U J
```

◇ Bonus Trivia

What is Christ's saying about the coming night?

"The night cometh, when no man can work." (John 9:4)

Word Search Answers

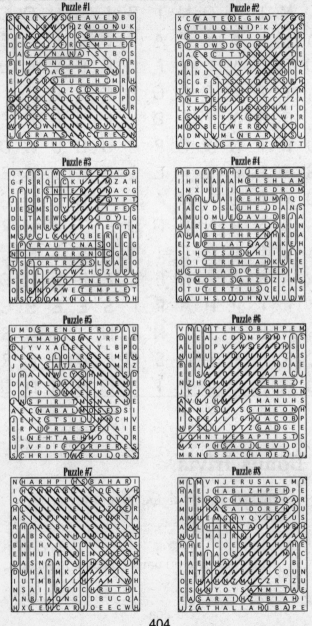

404

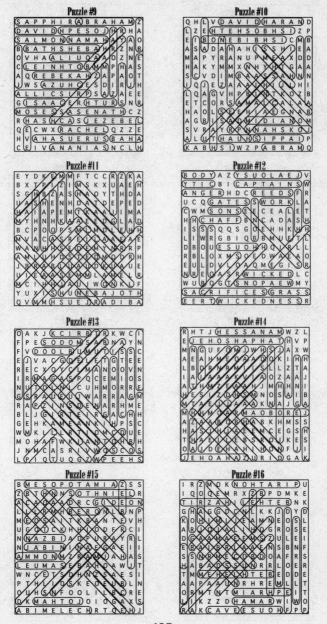

405

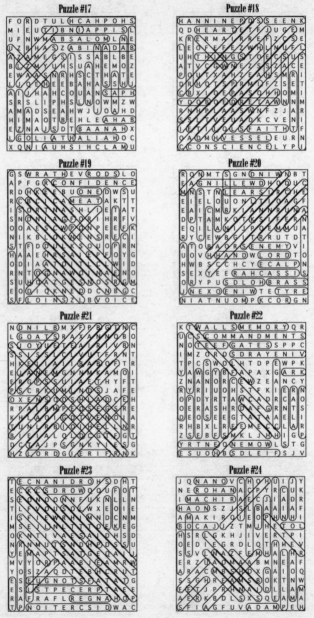

406

Puzzle #25

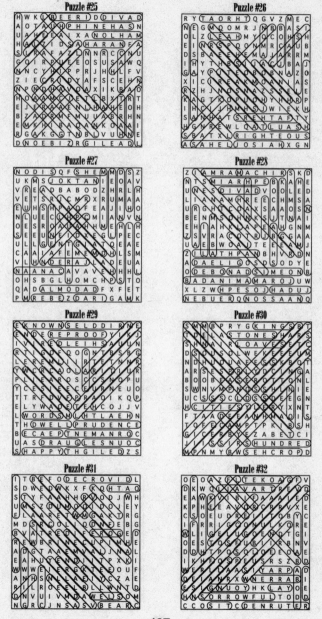

Puzzle #26

Puzzle #27

Puzzle #28

Puzzle #29

Puzzle #30

Puzzle #31

Puzzle #32

407

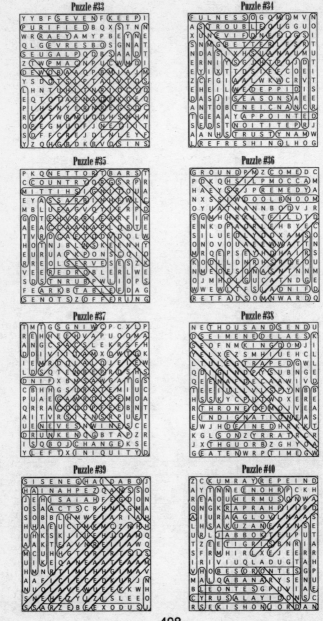

408

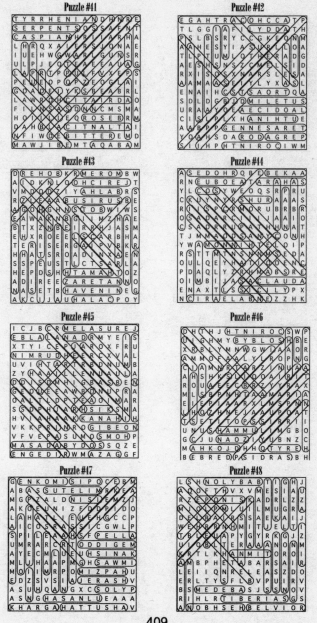

409

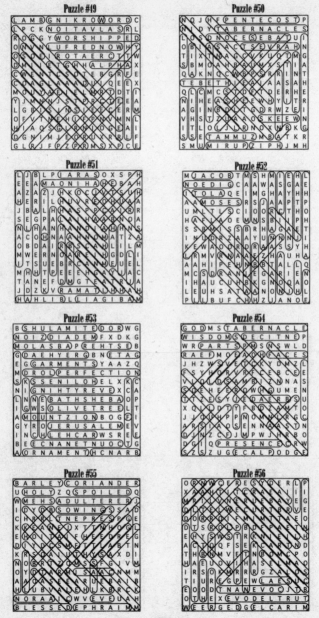

410

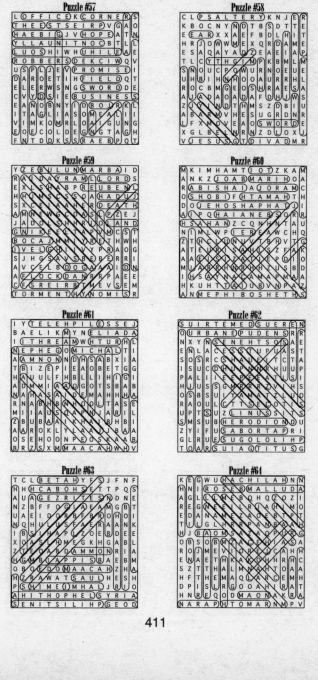

411

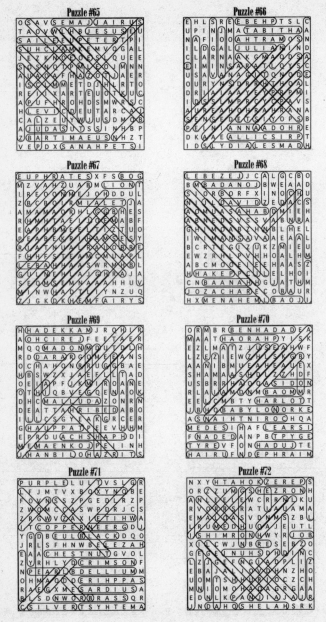

Puzzle #65

Puzzle #66

Puzzle #67

Puzzle #68

Puzzle #69

Puzzle #70

Puzzle #71

Puzzle #72

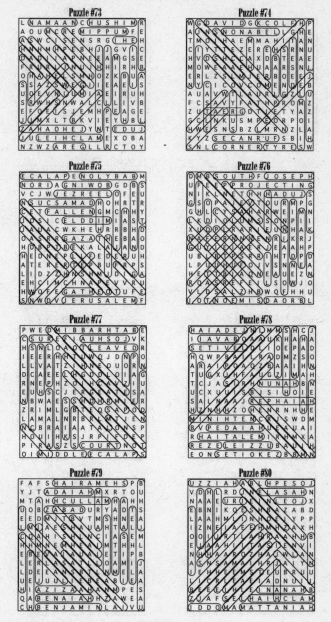

413

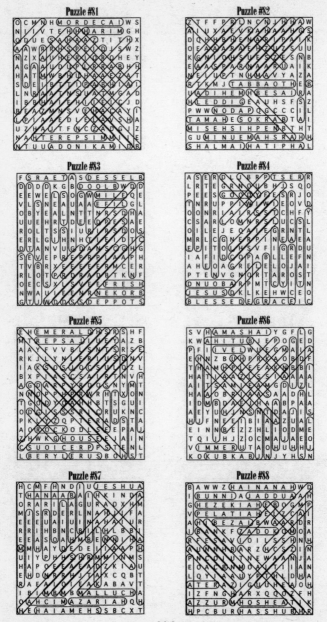

414

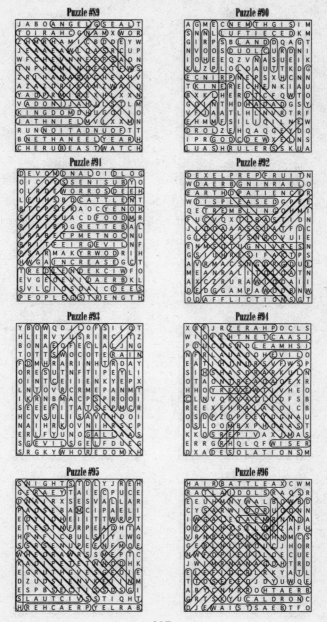

415

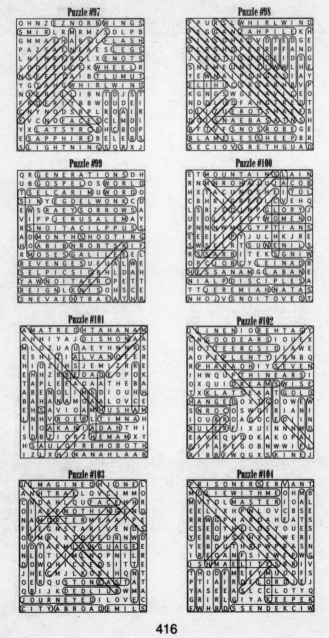

416

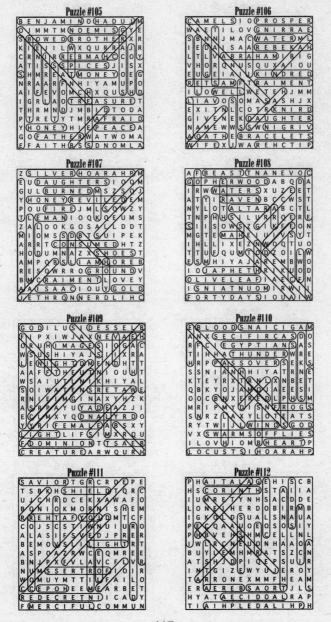

Puzzle #105

Puzzle #106

Puzzle #107

Puzzle #108

Puzzle #109

Puzzle #110

Puzzle #111

Puzzle #112

417

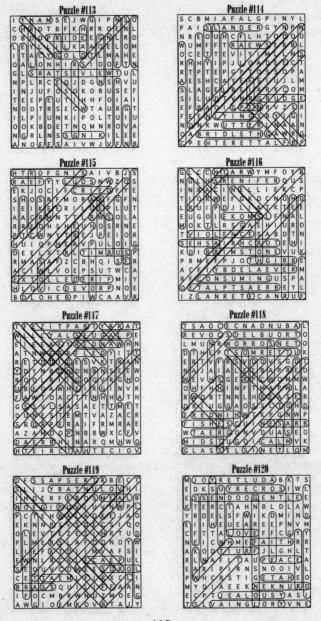

418

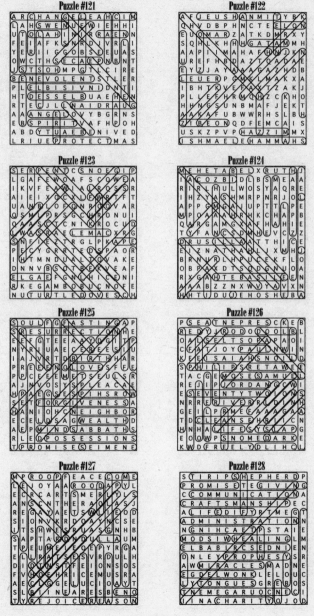

Puzzle #121

Puzzle #122

Puzzle #123

Puzzle #124

Puzzle #125

Puzzle #126

Puzzle #127

Puzzle #128

419

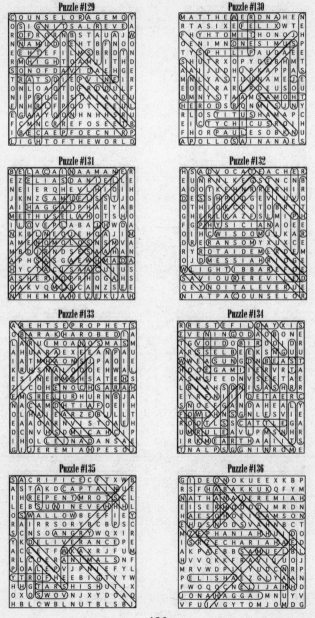

420

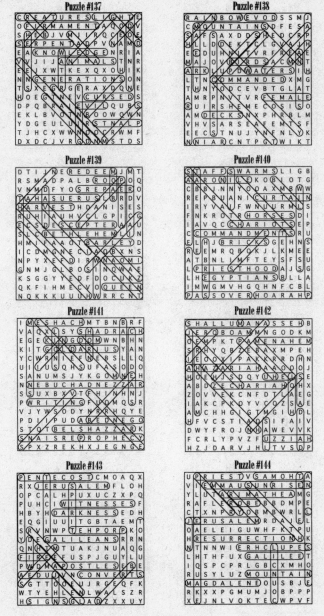

421

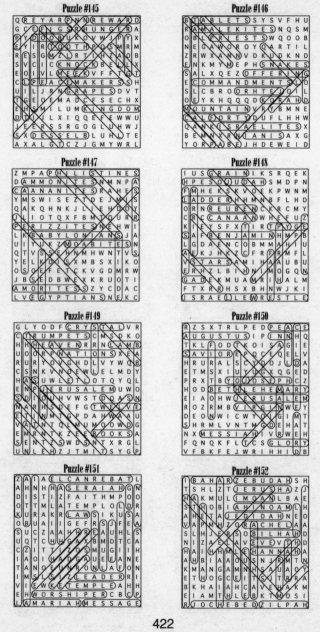

Puzzle #145

Puzzle #146

Puzzle #147

Puzzle #148

Puzzle #149

Puzzle #150

Puzzle #151

Puzzle #152

422

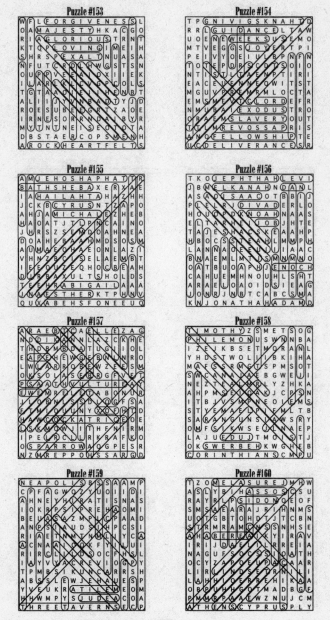

423

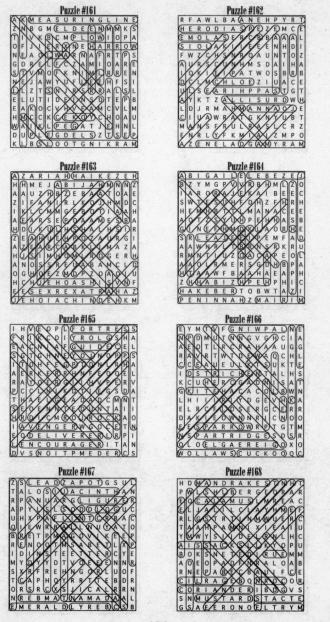

424

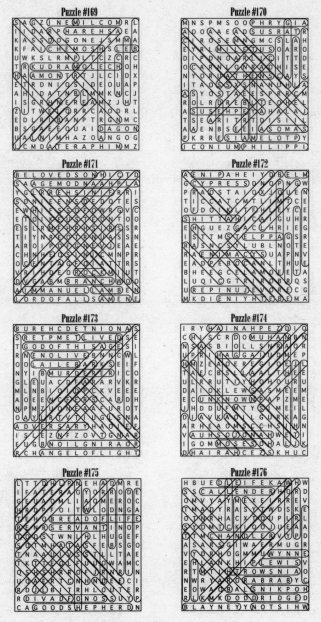

425

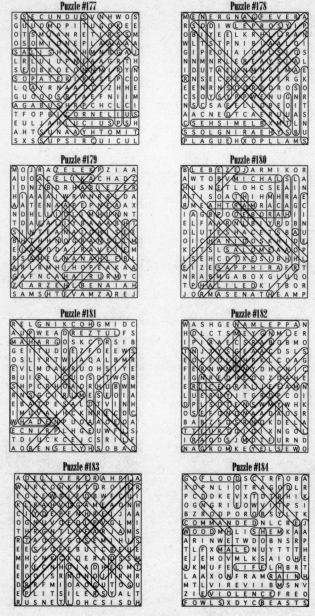

426

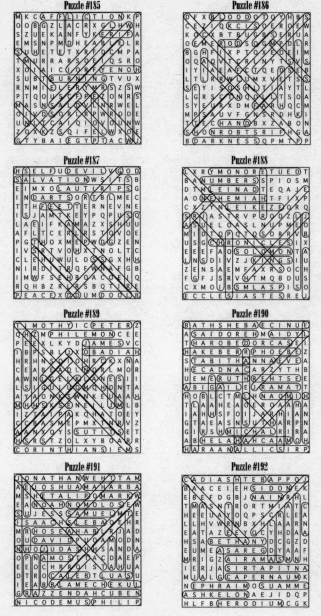

427

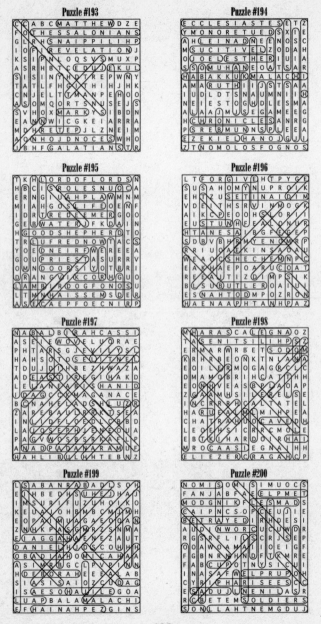

428